REVISED FOURTH EDITION

FLEA MARKET
TRADER

REVISED FOURTH EDITION

FLEA MARKET TRADER

Edited by Steve Quertermous

COLLECTOR BOOKS

P.O. Box 3009
Paducah, KY 42001

The current values in this book should be used only as a guide. They are not intended to set prices, which vary from one section of the country to another. Auction prices as well as dealer prices vary greatly and are affected by condition as well as demand. Neither the Author nor the Publisher assumes responsibility for any losses that might be incurred as a result of consulting this guide.

Printed by IMAGE GRAPHICS, Paducah, Kentucky

CONTENTS

Foreword 6

Categories 7

Sources for more information 277

Photograph & illustration acknowledgements 281

General Index 285

FOREWORD

I am a true collector. I'm not the type with a specialized interest and supportive bankroll that allows me to "swoop down" on flea markets and antique shows scooping up everything within my reach, leaving behind dealers counting handfulls of money. I am, instead, that breed that delights in everything old and loves even the not-so-old that triggers nostalgic memories and clutters up rooms. Like all true collectors, I am near Utopia scavenging through stacks of old papers that relatives find in attics and intend to send to the dump, or scouring flea markets and yard sales looking for underpriced items that I can attempt to bargain even lower.

My worst enemies -- the trash can and the effect of time itself -- constantly gnaw at my unsecured treasures and I grow indignant at the thought of someone arriving at a sale too early or out-bidding me at an auction. The very nature of my collecting habits proves that I'll never be able to reap even a small fortune for my stash of collectibles. But, on the other hand, sell is something that doesn't enter into my overall plan except to remove some less loved objects to finance new finds.

Maybe I'm not really a collector at all -- merely a saver. And like all saver-collectors, I guess my deep-down, ultimate goal is saving the secure past against some terrifying unknown future.

Advertising Collectible

The multimillion dollar advertising industry in America has provided the collector with an infinite number of trays, toys, signs, mirrors, buttons, cards, and other novelties. Anything featuring the advertiser's name is considered collectible, whether it is an ad torn from a magazine or one of the many items given away as sales aids or premiums. Give-aways from the Coca-Cola Company still head the list of popular advertising collectibles followed closely by other soft drink companies. Beer advertising and cigarette advertising are also very popular. Planters' "Mr. Peanut" items are increasing rapidly in popularity. Beware of reproductions.

A die cut advertising sign from the early 1900's. $35.00-40.00.

Chase & Sanborn, booklet of plantations & operations,
1880's $10.00-15.00
James S. Kirk Co. (soap), calendar of famous actors,
1890's $8.00-10.00
Fro-Joy Ice Cream, poster, card-playing couples,
1920's $15.00-20.00
Quaker Oats, booklet, puzzle pictures,
1900's $10.00-15.00
Arm & Hammer Soda, poster, birds,
17"x25" 15.00-20.00
De Laval, tin cut-outs, cow and calf $25.00-35.00
Oh Boy Gum, tin sign, boy and elf,
7"x15" $70.00-80.00
Red Goose Shoes, procelain sign, red goose $225.00-250.00
Mail Pouch Tobacco, tin thermometer, 1950's . $40.00-50.00
Heinz Pickles, pickle-shaped pin $7.00-10.00
Carter Ink, blotter,
1930's $1.00-2.00

Gillette Safety Razor, mirror round $15.00-20.00
Beechnut Gum, sign, lady with glass,
1930's $40.00-50.00
Philip Morris, cardboard stand-up, Johnny the Bellhop . . $20.00-30.00
Pepsi-Cola, recipe book,
1940 . . . . $10.00-12.00
Camel Cigarettes, tin thermometer, raised pack $25.00-30.00
Del Monte Canned Fruits, trolley wall sign, 1920's $50.00-60.00
Weatherbird Shoes, tape measure $20.00-25.00
Welch's Grape Juice, etched glass tumbler $15.00-20.00
Duffy's Whiskey,
mirror $20.00-25.00
Goodrich Tires, ashtray in rubber tire $10.00-15.00
Salada Tea, porcelain sign, shape of

This 2″ Star Soap mirror is worth about $35.00 and the O.V.B. Cutlery advertising mirror is worth $15.00-20.00. The tray from Boston's Hotel Plaza would probably bring between $25.00-35.00.

An early tin Dr. Pepper sign, approximately 1′x2′, is worth from $80.00 to $95.00.

tea box $50.00-60.00

Prudential Insurance, pin tray, Rock of Gibraltar . . . $15.00-20.00

Owensboro Wagons, tin sign, girl picking apples, 26″x38″ . . . . $750.00+

Lipton's Teas, cardboard sign, 17″x23″, 1890's . . . $100.00-125.00

Blue Jay Corn Plasters, cardboard stand-up, old man in

chair $125.00-150.00

Alta Coffee, tin sign, can shape $25.00-30.00

Howell's Root Beer, tin sign, bottle shape $40.00-50.00

Prince Albert Tobacco, paper sign, Indian $150.00-165.00

Old Reliable Coffee, change tray, man in red jacket $30.00-35.00

This large figural Royal Crown Cola scale is plastic on a cast iron base. Standing about 4′ tall it is an example of one of the more unusual forms of soda advertising and is worth around $1,000.00.

Akro Agate

Akro Agate was a producer of Depression Glass, marbles, and children's dishes. Some pieces are opaque and have a "marbleized" look to them. Entire sets of children's dishes in the original boxes are premium items, especially Play Time and American Maid tea sets. Some pieces are marked with a crow flying through the letter A, carrying a marble in its beak and each claw.

Children's dishes

Akro Luster, teapot with
   lid $15.00-18.00
Raised Daisy, tumbler,
   2″ $18.00-20.00
Octagonal, sugar with
   lid $8.00-10.00
Concentric ring, creamer,
   1¼″ $3.00-5.00

Stacked Disc, pitcher . . .$5.00-10.00
Interior panel, plate,
   3¼″ $3.00-5.00
Marbleized, creamer,
   1¼″ $20.00-25.00
Miss America, saucer . .$10.00-15.00
Lemonade and oxblood, cup and
   saucer $20.00-25.00
Topaz Trans Optic, teapot with
   lid $10.00-15.00
Jade Trans Optic, tumbler
   2″ $5.00-7.00
Azure Trans Optic, cereal bowl,
   3-3/8″ $15.00-20.00

Miscellanous

Goodrich ashtray &
   tire $8.00-10.00
Vase, ribbed 8″ $15.00-30.00
Cornucopia, 3¼″ $1.00-3.00
Scotty dog, puff box,
   white $35.00-45.00

Akro Agate children's dishes. This set is opaque and most of the individual pieces are worth about $5.00-15.00. The entire set is valued at $100.00-200.00.

Ashtray, shell shape $2.00-4.00
Bell, 5" $40.00-45.00
Colonial Lady, puff box,
    pink $25.00-35.00
Urn, 3¼" $2.00-4.00

Autographs

Autographs and autographed documents and photos of the famous are treasures to some collectors. Many types of personalities are considered collectible, whether it be sports figures, presidents, historical figures or motion picture stars. Values fluctuate greatly and rapidly in this category, especially in items considered to be rare. Age is not the only consideration when evaluating an autograph. The importance or popularity of the individual, the type of document involved and the number of the individual's autographs available have much influence on the market value. The prices here should be used as a comparative guide. Be especially careful to avoid forgeries and misrepresentations in this area.

Old stock certificates and other documents are good sources for autographs.

Winston Churchill, English Prime
    Minister $30.00-50.00
Duke Ellington, band
    leader $7.00-10.00
Spiro Agnew, letter signed while
    Vice President $50.00-100.00
Bing Crosby, signed
    photo $100.00-125.00
Harry Houdini, magician,
    letter $125.00-150.00
Joe Louis, boxer $10.00-12.00
Lyndon Johnson,
    signature $10.00-12.00
Jayne Mansfield,
    actress $10.00-12.00
Warren Harding, signed
    photo $100.00-125.00
William McKinley, letter while
    president .... $300.00 +
Arthur Conan Doyle,
    signature $35.00-45.00
John Glenn Jr., astronaut, signature

JANUARY 20, 1973

Richard Nixon's signature will probably be one of great value in years to come due to his unprecedented leave of office. Presidential signatures from an "autopen" are worth considerably less than an acutal autograph.

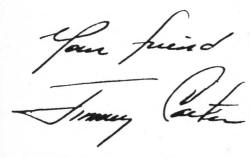

Another living former President, Jimmy Carter. Signatures of political figures are usually worth more if the autograph is on a document written while the individual was in office.

Literary figures are popular with collectors. This is the signature of the famous novelist John Steinbeck.

on Project Mercury
cover $15.00-20.00
Thomas Nast, editorial cartoonist,
signature $10.00-12.00
Mae West, signed
photo $25.00-35.00
William F. Cody, Buffalo Bill
signature on
program $65.00-75.00
Annie Oakley,
signature $60.00-75.00
Jacqueline Kennedy,
signature $20.00-30.00
Carole Lombard, signed
letter $150.00-200.00
Calvin Coolidge, letter signed while
President . . . . $200.00+
J. Edgar Hoover,
signature $12.00-15.00

Automobile Collectibles

Since the price of antique automobiles is very restrictive to most collectors, many have turned to collecting materials dealing with autmobiles. Actual accessories as well as owners manuals, shop manuals, advertisements, catalogs and posters featuring the cars of yesterday have become very collectible. Anything made through the 1950's and even 60's is considered collectible and even some later items. But, generally, the more valuable items are from the 1930's or before. Be on the lookout for items from or about automobiles or their producing companies that are no longer in existence.

Instruction manual, Knox 1904 Model
C, 24 pages $35.00-5.00
Catalog, Pierce Arrow,
1937 . . . . $45.00-50.00
Porcelain sign, Oldsmobile, 42″
round $75.00-85.00
Hubcap, Ford Model T . . $3.00-5.00
Brochure, Dodge Charger,
1968 . . . . $3.00-5.00
Horn, Model A Ford . . $15.00-20.00
Grille emblem, 1938 Cadillac
V-16 . . . . $10.00-15.00
Ford News magazine,
1930's $3.00-5.00
Brochure, Ford, 1940 . . $10.00-12.00

1953 Plymouth catalog. Material from the 1950's and 1960's is becoming more collectible as time passes.

Automobile flower holders can be found in carnival glass and crystal most readily. This matched pair is worth about $60.00-85.00.

Hood ornament, Dodge Ram,
1930's $55.00-60.00
Brochure, Packard,
1920's $15.00-18.00
Catalog, Pierce Arrow,
1930's $50.00-55.00
Radiator cap, Ford, brass,
1920 . . . . $20.00-30.00
Hood ornament, Pontiac,
1950's $30.00-40.00
Tire pump, Ford $10.00-15.00
Catalog, Oldsmobile,
1934 . . . . $30.00-40.00
Owners manual, Cadillac,
1930's $10.00-12.00
Running board, luggage
racks $5.00-10.00
Radiator cap, Pontiac,
1920's $15.00-20.00
Tire gauge, dial type $8.00-10.00

Aviation Collectibles

Anything dealing with airplanes and flight, either civilian or military, is highly collectible. Items concerning zeppelins or lighter-than-air craft are especially popular among aviation collectors. Lindberg and related materials are also popular items, and there is a multitude of collectibles available in this area.

Time table, Northwest Airlines,
1944 . . . . $3.00-5.00
Shot glass, Southern
Airlines $5.00-7.00
Postcard, American Airlines,
sleeper plane $2.00-4.00
Folder, United Airlines
737 . . . . $3.00-5.00
Airline schedule, American Airlines,
April 1937 . . . . $3.00-5.00
Amelia Earhart, framed
photo $10.00-15.00
Folder, Douglas Aircraft Corp.,
1940's $5.00-7.00
Time Table, TWA,
1940 . . . . $4.00-5.00
Postcard, Spirit of St. Louis and
Lindbergh $10.00-12.00
Postcard, U.S. Fighter planes in air,
WWII $7.00-10.00
Aircraft yearbook,
1942 . . . . $12.00-15.00
New York Airways, helicopter service
schedule, 1950's $3.00-5.00
Advertising brochure, Beechcraft
Bonanza $5.00-7.00
Stick doll, wood, Pan Am,
3½ " $2.00-3.00
Stewardess doll, American Airlines,
plastic, 12 ", 1960's $5.00-7.00
Magazine, *Aerial Age Weekly*,

Luftwaffe Glider Pilot Badge. This badge was presented to those who completed train-ing and became qulaified glider pilots. This Nazi aviation relic is worth about $1,000.00.

1919-1921 .... $5.00-10.00

Magazine, *Flying,*
   pre-1965 .... $.50-1.00

Book, *War Wings*, 1937 $5.00-10.00

Book, *Air Service Boys,* any of the
   series, 1920 .... $3.00-5.00

Postcard, Piper Tri-Pacer,
   1955 .... $1.00-2.00

Book, *The Airship Boys in Barren
   Lands,* 1910 .... $8.00-10.00

Book, *Wings Over the Andes,*
   1939 .... $5.00-7.00

Avon

Avon began as the California Perfume Company in the 1880's and has grown to become one of the largest perfume manufacturers and distributors in the world. Collectors across the country consider these products collectible and many, especially early products, are quite valuable to the serious collector. Perfume bottles are popular and so are food coloring kits, soaps, nearly any figural container and many other Avon

The Avon Warrior Head on the left is from 1968 and is frosted. $3.00-5.00. The Warrior Head on the right is from 1967 and has a silver-colored helmet. $9.00-15.00.

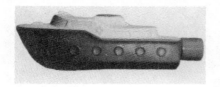

Avon S.S. Suds. A blue and white shampoo container, this plastic bottle is valued at $2.00-4.00.

Reginald Raccoon III. This floating soap dish and soap from 1970 is worth about $3.50.

products. Prices haven't increased much in this area in the last year or so.

Astringent, clear glass, aqua lid,
1936 . . . . $10.00-15.00
Blue Lotus, after bath, 8″, clear,
1967 . . . . $5.00-8.00
Humpty Dumpty Bubble Bath,
1963 . . . . $5.00-7.00

Clock Bubble Bath,
1961 . . . . $5.00-7.00
Perry Penguin soap dish and
soap $8.00-10.00
Pluto Shampoo, 1970 . . . . $3.00-5.00
Cash register shampoo,
1970 . . . . $2.00-3.00
Royal Jasmine Bath Salts,
1954 . . . . $20.00-25.00
Skin-So-Soft Dophin,
1968 . . . . $5.00-7.00
To-A-Wild-Rose body, powder
1954 . . . . $8.00-10.00
Bay Rum jug, 1962 . . . . $10.00-15.00
Gavel, after shave,
1967 . . . . $12.00-15.00
Bowling Pin, after shave,
1969 . . . . $4.00-5.00
Embossed Stage Coach, after shave,
1960 . . . . $20.00-25.00
Dueling set, cologne,
1967 . . . . $25.00-30.00
Steam Boat, after shave,
1971 . . . . $6.00-8.00
Stage Coach, after shave,
1970 . . . . $3.00-5.00
Spongaroo, soap and sponge,
1966 . . . . $10.00-12.00
Black Sheep set, 1955 . . $50.00-60.00
Western Saddle, after shave,
1971 . . . . $7.00-8.00

Badges

Collectors have gradually picked up law enforcement badges until they are now considered to be popular items. Once only popular with collectors of old west memorabilia, badges are now collectible on their own merit. Most collectible of the badges are those in gold or silver, but nickel, brass or combinations are also very popular. Unusual badges, express badges, and old badges from famous western towns are much sought by collectors. The collector should be careful to purchase

Law enforcement stars and shields worth about $50.00-150.00 each.

Another group of law enforcement badges. $50.00-$150.00 each.

only authentic badges because there are some reproductions on the market.

Gold presentation badge, Baltimore City Police Commissioner, 1890's $1500.00
Star, Chicago Police Lieutenant $50.00-100.00
Eagle & Shield, Police Captain, East St. Louis $75.00-100.00
Shield, El Paso Police . $50.00-75.00
Star, Joliet Police $75.00-100.00
Star, Los Angeles Police $50.00-75.00
Star w/ball points, Arizona Territorial Ranger . $100.00-150.00
Oval w/scroll, Boston Special Police $100.00-150.00
Star, police, silver 1870's $200.00-225.00
"Bumper" badge, Illinois Police, star, bronze, 1920's $25.00-30.00
Sergeant, Eagle, Indian and ship, Chicago $75.00-125.00
"Bumper" badge, Chief of Police, Forest Park, IL, 1920's or 30's $25.00-35.00
"Bumper" badge, Special Deputy, Cook County, 1920's or 30's $25.00-35.00
Star in circle, Deputy U.S. Marshal $100.00-125.00
Scrolled shield, Special Deputy, Cambria County . . . $75.00-125.00

Banks, Mechanical

Mechanical banks are iron, brightly colored banks that perform some kind of action when a coin is placed in the bank. There are between 235 and 250 known types of mechanical banks produced between the Civil War and World War I. Be very cautions because many reproductions have been produced. Though most of these reproduc-

Teddy And The Bear mechanical bank. when the hunter shoots the coin into the tree, the bear pops out the top. $250.00 and up.

The Stamp Speaker mechanical bank, $500.00 and up.

tions can be distinguised from the old banks, many are made to appear as the originals.

William Tell $325.00
Professor Pug Frog's Great Bicycle Feat . . . . $500.00+
Football . . . . $500.00+
Butting Buffalo . . . . $500.00+

Mechanical banks. Santa Claus at The Chimeny, $325.00 and up; Speaking Dog, $275.00 and up.

Dog & Turn Table $225.00
Chief Big Moon . . . . $500.00 +
Man riding Elephant $225.00
Mason Bank $500.00
Indian & Bear $300.00
Punch & Judy $300.00
Atlas Bank $375.00
Hoop-La $350.00
Magician $375.00
Stump Speaker $325.00
Artillery Bank $300.00
Lion Hunter . . . . $500.00 +
Dancing Bear . . . . $500.00 +
World's Fair $375.00
Chinaman $375.00
Squirrel $400.00
Grenadier $300.00
Organ Grinder & Monkey . . $300.00
Acrobat $350.00
Mother & Baby Eagles $325.00
Uncle Sam $300.00
Lion & Monkeys $300.00
Darktown Battery $325.00
Trick Pony . . . . $300.00 +
Trick Dog . . . . $300.00 +

This barrel bank advertises Midwestern Savings and Loan and is from the 1940's. $12.00-18.00.

Banks, Still

Still banks are generally constructed of tin, cast iron, aluminum, pot metal, or glass and have no working parts with the exception of wheels. They were

Cast iron bulldog bank. Figural animal banks were very popular when cast iron examples were readily available.

produced in a variety of styles and types, from characters to buildings, cars and animals. Following the war years, military vehicles and heroes were very popular. Some banks were used as advertisement and given away as premiums. Value depends on rarity, quality and type, as well as condtion.

Baseball player....... $80.00-100.00
Elephant, iron, 3"..... $40.00-45.00
Top hat, iron......... $60.00-65.00
Saddled donkey, 4½".. $80.00-85.00
Battleship, iron, 6".. $200.00-225.00
Lion, cast iron, 3".... $30.00-40.00
Lion on tub $65.00-75.00
Deer, iron........... $85.00-100.00
American Indian, iron . $80.00-85.00
Rabbit, sitting, iron . $150.00-175.00
Buffalo, iron $75.00-80.00
Tank, WWI style...... $75.00-85.00
Elephant with wheels,
    iron, 4".......... $200.00-225.00

Clown, iron $65.00-70.00
Soldier, iron, 6" $250.00-275.00
Sailor, iron, 6" $175.00-185.00
Mickey Mouse Post Office,
    cylindrical, tin $50.00-70.00
Rabbit, standing $75.00-100.00
Trolley car $200.00-225.00
Rhinoceros, iron $250.00-275.00

Barber Collectibles

Barber and grooming collectibles include items for home use as well as those used solely in barbershops. Shaving mugs were popular in the latter part of the 19th century and demand high prices when found in good condition. Barbershop furnishings and barber tools are also picking up a large following.

Towel sterilizer, nickel & copper,
    1900's .... $500.00+
Wood pole, red & white, ball on

Barber Collectible. In the bank hand curlers and a barber's brush. In the foreground a straight razor, hand clippers, a razor blade safe and safety razor blade.

each end, 1800's . . $100.00-125.00
Shaving mug,
    occupational $150.00-300.00
Brush, wood handle, buffalo hair,
    early 1900's $20.00-30.00
Hand clippers, metal,
    1920's or 1930's $15.00-25.00
Hand curler, wood
    handles $15.00-20.00
Bottle, porcelain,
    "Bay Rum" $60.00-70.00
Catalog, Theodore Kochs Co., 1923
    barber supplies $50.00-60.00
Catalog, Kocken Barbers Supply,
    shaving mugs $40.00-50.00
Shaving stand, brass & mahogony,
    marble top, tilting mirror,
    1860's . . . . $600.00 +
Magazine ad, Mulsified Cocoanut Oil
    Shampoo, 1917 . . . . . . $4.00-5.00
Straight Razors, pair of Joseph
    Rodgers & Sons, in satin lined case,
    1860's $50.00-60.00
Barber Chair, walnut on platform,
    horsehair padding,
    1870's $1,500.00

Baseball Cards

Baseball cards were first issued in the United States before the turn of the Century. They were small, around 1½ "x2½ ", generally of poor quality and given away with tobacco and cigarettes. In the 1930's, chewing gum companies began to produce baseball cards and have continued to date, most popular card producers being Bowman and Topps. The most treasured cards are the color, photo cards of the 1930's. Any baseball great or Hall of Famer is considerably more valuable than the common players in a particular issue year.

Bowman, 1950, color,

A 1953 color Bowman card of Casey Stengel.

Topps 1954 Willie Mays baseball card.

21

Sandy Koufax

Sandy Koufax from the Topps 1958 series.

2 1/8″x2½″ $1.50-3.00	
Bowman, 1951, color,	
2 1/8″x3 1/8″ $1.50-4.50	
Bowman, 1952, color	
2 1/8″x3 1/8″ $1.00-2.25	
Bowman, 1953, black and white,	
2½″x3 3/4″ $2.50-7.00	

Bowman, 1954, color
2½″x3 3/4″ ....50¢-$1.00
Bowman, 1955, color
2½″x3 3/4″ ....50¢-$1.00
Topps, 1952, color
2 5/8″x3 5/8″ $2.00-5.00
Topps, 1953, color
2 5/8″x3 5/8″ $1.00-5.00
Topps, 1954, color
2 5/8″x3 5/8″ $1.00-1.25
Topps, 1955, color
2 5/8″x3 5/8″ ....50¢-$1.00
Topps, 1956, color
2 5/8″x3 5/8″ ....50¢-$1.50
Topps, 1957, color
2½″x3½″ ....25¢-$1.50
Topps, 1958, color
2½″x3½″ ....25¢-50¢
Topps, 1959, color,
2½″x3½″ ....25¢-$1.00
Topps, 1960, color,
2½″x3½″ ....25¢-$1.00
Topps, 1961, color,
2½″x3½″ ....25¢-$2.50
Topps, 1962, color,
2½″x3½″ ....25¢-$1.00
Topps, 1963, 1964, color,
2½″x3½″ ....10¢-75¢
Topps, 1965, color,

The Topps 1960 cards were horizontal. This one features Ernie Banks.

Cereal cards are sometimes difficult to find in excellent condition due to their very nature. This Mickey Mantle card is from Post Cereal's 1961 set.

1963 Post Cereal card with Juan Marichal.

2½ "x3½ " . . . . .10¢-25¢
Topps, 1966, 1967, color,
   2½ "x3½ " . . . . .10¢-$1.00
Topps, 1968 to present, color,
   2½ "x3½ " . . . . .10¢-25¢
Post Cereal, 1961, 1962, 1963,
   2½ "x3½ " . . . . .25¢-50¢

Baseball Collectibles

The memorabilia of America's national pastime has come into the limelight as popular collectibles. The ticket stubs, player autographs, programs, scorecards, fan magazines, yearbooks, match books, photographs, postcards, uniforms, pins and trading cards of baseball have become very collectible, with values increasing. Teams no longer in existence are good to look for and so are mementoes of the more popular players and Hall of Famers.

1963 St. Louis Cardinal yearbook.

Mickey Mantle, plastic Hartland
statue, 1960's $50.00-80.00
Magazine, *Street & Smith Yearbook,*
1962 . . . . $3.00-5.00
Yearbook, Baltimore Orioles,
1959 . . . . $8.00-10.00
Bobby Richardson, metal coin,
Topps, 1964 . . . . $2.00-5.00

Program, New York Yankees,
1961 . . . . $2.00-5.00
Booklets, DX Premiums, 1960's,
Pitching, Catching,
etc. . . . . $1.50-2.50 each
T shirt, Mantle & Maris,
1961 . . . . $4.00-5.00
Bob Gibson,

St. Louis Cardinal scorecard from the early 1960's.

autographed photo $3.00-5.00
World Series program, 1942,
  Cardinals/Yankees . . $30.00-60.00
Autographed baseball, 1956,
  Yankees $30.00-60.00
Booklet, *Dizzy Baseball,*
  by Dizzy Dean,
  1950's $5.00-10.00
Ticket stub, 1959 World Series,
  White Sox $3.00-5.00
Yearbook, Philadelpia Athletics,
  Elephant on cover,
  1953 . . . . $3.00-5.00
Magazine, *Facts Figures Rules, Major
  League Baseball,*
  1940's $10.00-15.00
Program, Boston Red Sox,
  1951 . . . . $2.00-3.00
Ticket stub, 1934 World Series,
  St. Louis Cardinals . . $10.00-15.00
Magazine advertisement, Camel

cigarettes, 1956, shows players
  with cigarettes $1.00-3.00
Autograph, Babe Ruth,
  1930's . . . . $100.00+
Pinback button, Boston Red Sox,
  1946 . . . . $5.00-7.50
Autographed baseball,
  Lou Gehrig . . . . $200.00+

Baskets

Appreciation of basketry in the past decade has led to an increased interest in collecting baskets. Old handmade baskets are the most popular with Shaker examples at a premium. Watch out for reproduction made to appear old.

Swing handle basket, square bottom,
  round top, oak
  splint $250.00-300.00
Cheese basket, hexgon, open weave,
  26″ round $375.00-450.00
Open weave gathering basket,
  oak splint, notch
  handles $135.00-450.00
Utility basket, rye straw, coil

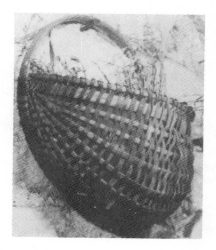

This half basket is worth about $100.00-125.00.

This egg basket is of the type commonly referred to as a buttocks style. It is from the late 1800's and made of oak splint. $175.00-200.00.

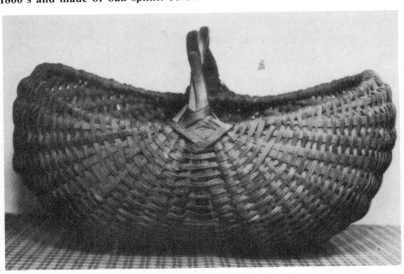

An ash storage or gathering basket with double wrapped hickory handle from New England, late 1800's. $300.00.

construction, hickory
handle $140.00-160.00
Field basket, New England, 32″x16″,
woven handles $300.00-350.00
Half basket with wood

handle $90.00-115.00
Utility basket, ash splint, woven,
Shaker $110.00-120.00
Garden basket, braided handle,
oak splint, rib

Field basket with unusual braided handle. $275.00-300.00.

Shaker feather-type basket. $150.00-165.00.

Oak splint winnowing basket. $375.00-450.00.

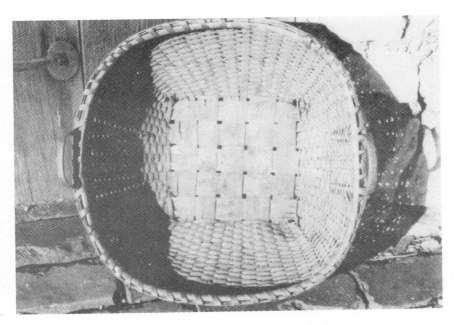

Storage basket for fruits or vegetables. $80.00-95.00.

construction $275.00-300.00
Buttocks egg baket, oak splint,
   splint handle $120.00-135.00
Swing handle basket, double rim,
   ash splint $225.00-250.00
Knife & fork basket, oak splint,
   carved handle $140.00-175.00
Sewing basket, demi-john bottom,
   hickory handles, double
   rim $125.00-140.00
Nantucket "lightship" basket,
   rib construction,
   swing handle $350.00-400.00
Herb tray, oak splint,
   wrapped rim $125.00-140.00
Field basket, open plaited bottom,
   28″ diameter $375.00-400.00
Fruit drying basket, pine frame,
   ash splint $350.00-400.00
Garden basket, plaited oak splint,
   wrapped rim $85.00-95.00
Field basket, oval, 22″,
   carved handle, plaited oak
   splint $200.00-225.00
Storage basket, oak splint,
   twig handle $100.00-115.00
Field basket, 31″ diameter,
   oak splint, carved
   handle $175.00-215.00

Beatles Collectibles

The Beatles sprang into the American music scene in the early 1960's and almost immediately the public was bombarded with Beatle products. In addition to the early records, many promotional items are now relatively scarce and, naturally, demand high prices. Almost anything associated with the Beatles is collectible, especially early items.

Doll, rubber with hair, facsimile
   autograph on guitar,
   Paul $20.00-30.00

Scale model, plastic, mint in box,
   any Beatle $35.00-40.00
Beatle cards, mid 1960's . . 50¢-$1.00
Lunch box & thermos, tin, color
   illustration of
   Beatles $25.00-30.00
Beatle wig in original
   package $25.00-35.00
Beatles Diary, color photo on
   cover $10.00-12.00
Autographed photo of all four
   Beatles $700.00
Magazine, *Saturday Evening Post*,
   March 1964, Beatles
   cover $10.00-12.00
Pinback button,
   "I Love the Beatles" . $5.00-10.00
Book, *All about the Beatles*,
   1964 . . . . $7.00-10.00

Beatle card from the 1960's.

Beer Cans

Beer can collecting is an especially popular hobby today, particularly among younger collectors. It is a reasonably inexpensive hobby to begin but some of the early or more rare cans can bring prices of up to $100.00 or more. Most beer cans are colorful with

12 ounce cone top beer cans. Top row, left to right: ABC Beer, $175.00; Areo Club, $100.00; Altes Lager, $40.00; American, $100.00; Barbarossa, $95.00; Bavarians Old Style, $60.00; Beckers Unita Club, $110.00; Berghoff, 1877, $40.00. Bottom row, left to right: Berghoff, 1887, $30.00; Beverwyck, $50.00; Beverwyck Irish, $50.00; Billings Pale, $200.00; Black Forest Light, $200.00; Blackhawk Topping, $75.00; Black Lable $50.00; Blatz Old Heidelberg Castle, $35.00.

Beer Cans. Top row left to right: Fitgers, $6.00; Fitgers, $6.00; Fitz, $20.00; Fitzgerald Ale, $45.00; Fitzgerald, $25.00; 500 Ale, $75.00; Foodtown, $25.00; Fort Pitt, $15.00. Bottom row, left to right: Fort Schuyler, $40.00; Fox Brew, $15.00; Fox Deluxe, $85.00; Fox Deluxe, $20.00; remaining Fox Deluxe cans, $10.00-25.00.

unique designs and lend themselves well to display. The most popular cans are the cone top cans that were the earliest beer cans.

12 oz. cone top beer cans.

12 oz. cone top beer cans.

Goebel Bantam Beer,
  8 oz. $25.00-30.00
Blackhawk Premium Beer,
  12 oz. $100.00-125.00
Golden Gate, 11 or
  12 oz. $40.00-50.00
Jet Malt Liquor,
  11 or 12 oz. $10.00-15.00
Iroquois Draft Ale $30.00-35.00
Paul Bunyan $100.00-125.00
Red Fox Premium $75.00-80.00
Weisbrod $10.00-15.00
Whale's White Ale,
  white can $40.00-50.00
Zody's Premium
  Beer $100.00-125.00

Cone Tops

Buckeye Sparkling
  Dry $40.00-50.00
Berghoff 1887, 12 oz. . .$30.00-40.00
Fox Delux, 12 oz. $35.00-45.00
Haas Pilsner, 12 oz. . . .$70.00-80.00
Leinenkugel, 12 oz. $30.00-40.00

Old Topper Ale,
  12 oz. $150.00-175.00
Wooden Shoe Lager,
  12 oz. $30.00-40.00
Silver Cream, 12 oz. . . .$60.00-70.00
Krueger Finest Beer,
  12 oz. $40.00-50.00
Bon Premium Beer,
  12 oz. $200.00-225.00

Beer Collectibles

With the increased interest in beer cans, there has been an increasing concern over beer advertising and related materials. Trays, signs, taps, kegs, and so forth, have become popular with values steadily rising. The color and quality of the beer items, in addition to their relative abundance, have contributed strongly to this popularity. Currently beer advertising items remain high among the list of most sought after advertising collectibles.

Linsers Beer tin tray, 13"x10½". $50.00.

This Indianapolis Brewing Company tray is worth about $65.00-75.00.

A tin sign for Buckeye Beer, about 13″ in length. $25.00-30.00.

Adolphus Busch, pocketknife/
   corkscrew $50.00-60.00

Bernheimer & Schwartz Brewing
   Co., 1912
   calendar $300.00-325.00

Claussen Brewing, paper poster,
   draped lady & costumed
   man $225.00-250.00

Deppen Brewing Co., painting on
   glass, elk $300.00-325.00

Miller Beer, pen &
   pencil set $10.00-15.00

Old Milwaukee, tap
   knob $5.00-10.00

Blatz Beer, miniature
   bottle $10.00-12.00

Elk Run Brewing,
   tray, elk $125.00-135.00

Frank Fehr's Brewing, sign cardboard, 18″x24″ . . . $150.00-175.00

Goebel Brewing Co., change
   tray, Swiss man $90.00-100.00

Hiawatha Beer, embossed tin
   sign, 1901 . . . . $350.00-400.00

Indian Wharf Brewing, paper
   sign, 20″x29″ $250.00-275.00

Jax Beer, tray,
   cowboy $75.00-100.00

Liberty Beer, tray, Indian
   Princess $125.00-150.00

Oertle Brew, change tray,
   girl & dove $50.00-60.00

Pabst, paper under glass
   view of brewery .... $650.00+
George Ringler & Co.,
   calendar, 1915 .... $150.00-175.00
Rock Island Brewing,
   change tray $45.00-50.00
Adam Scheidt, paper poster,
   19"x29", soldiers .. $250.00-275.00
Schlitz, stained glass window, world
   globe trademark ..... $1,200.00+

Bells

Bells are made of many different materials and serve many different purposes. Though some bells were made entirely for decoration, most were created to inform the hearer of some event. There are bells to announce tea, bells to announce dinner, bells to announce the beginning of school and church and many more. Several types of metal have been used in making bells. Brass bells are especially popular.

#2 dinner bell $50.00-65.00

A school bell with maple handle.

Primitive cowbells with carved wooden clappers and leather collars.

Iron triangle, ranch
   bell $20.00-25.00
Ships bells, brass,
   8" $75.00-100.00
Locomotive bell, cast iron with
   yoke & stand .... $600.00+
Sleighbells, burnished brass, 23
   on leather strap ...... $250.00+

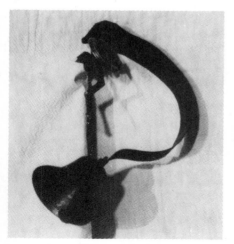

This shopbell from the 1800's was mounted above the door and rang when the door was opened.

Cowbell, brass with wood
  clapper $30.00-35.00
Shopbell, brass on iron spring,
  1880's $50.00-60.00
Goat bell, tin $5.00-10.00
Trolley car bell $75.00-100.00
Hotel tap bell, ornate,
  brass $75.00-100.00
Prize fight gong,
  brass $125.00-150.00
Fire engine bell,
  brass $125.00-150.00
School bell, brass,
  wood handle $35.00-45.00
Centennial, 1876,
  brass $100.00-125.00
Cut glass bell $80.00-100.00

Big Little Books

Big Little Books first appeared in the early 1930's. They are small, (4"x4") thick books that are generally illustrated with comic strips or movie stills and were produced under several different brand names. The most desirable of the little books are those from the "Golden Age" that lasted from the late 1930's until the late 1940's. Well known comic characters are very popular with collectors and usually bring good prices. Similar books are being produced today, so the collector of "Big Little Books" should be very cautious. All prices reflect books in good to very good condition produced before 1950.

Alley Oop, any $5.00-15.00
Betty Boop and Snow
  White $10.00-15.00
Big Chief Wahoo, any . . . $5.00-7.50
Blondie and Dagwood,
  any $10.00-15.00
Buck Jones in Night
  Riders $20.00-30.00

Buck Jones, all others . $10.00-15.00
Bugs Bunny, (first) $25.00-35.00
Bugs Bunny, all others . $12.00-18.00
Captain Easy, any $5.00-10.00
Captain Midnight, any . $12.00-15.00
Chester Gump, any $10.00-12.00
Dan Dunn, Secret Operative
  48, 1934 . . . . $20.00-25.00
Dan Dunn, any other . . . $7.00-10.00
Dick Tracy, Detective and
  Federal Agent $25.00-30.00
Adventure of Dick
  Tracy $30.00-35.00
Dick Tracy, Frozen Bullet
  Murders $25.00-30.00
Dick Tracy, Maroon Mask
  Gang $25.00-30.00
Dick Tracy, Mystery of the
  Purple Cross $35.00-45.00
Dick Tracy, all others . $15.00-25.00
Don Winslow, any $5.00-8.00
Donald Duck and the
  Ducklings $35.00-40.00

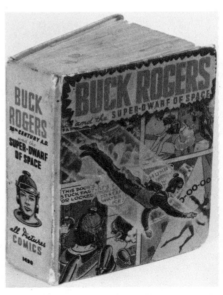

Buck Rogers is a popular character of Big Little Books. This example features the "Super Dwarf of Space".

36

Walter Lantz's popular Andy Panda is featured in this Big Little Book.

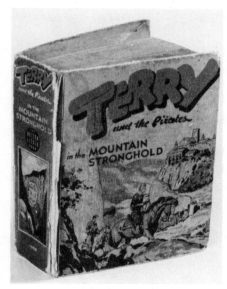

An adventure story of Terry and the Pirates is the subject of this Big Little Book.

Donald Duck, all
   others $15.00-20.00
Ellery Queen, any $10.00-15.00

Felix the Cat, any $7.50-12.50
Flash Gordon on Planet
   Mongo $45.00-60.00
Flash Gordon, all
   others $35.00-45.00
G-Man, any $10.00-15.00
Gene Autry in
   Gunsmoke $25.00-35.00
Gene Autry, all others . $12.50-17.50
Jungle Jim, any $12.50-17.50
King of the Royal
   Mounted $7.50-10.00
Little Orphan Annie,
   (first) $30.00-35.00
Little Orphan Annie,
   any other $20.00-25.00
Mickey Mouse, (first) . . $45.00-60.00
Mickey Mouse, all
   others $20.00-40.00
Popeye, any $15.00-20.00
Roy Rogers, any $10.00-15.00
Tarzan of the Apes $25.00-35.00
Tarzan, all others $12.00-15.00
Tom Mix $12.00-20.00
Woody Woodpecker, Big Game
   Hunter $10.00-15.00

Black Glass

Many major glass producers in this country made items in black. Some collectors have specialized in this glass and search for any item that is black.

A Westmoreland Glass Chicken sherbet. This piece of black glass from the late 1930's is valued at $16.00-18.00.

Heisey, Fenton, Cambridge and many other quality glass houses made candlesticks, compotes, console bowls, and many other pieces in black glass.

Cambridge "Calla Lily" candlesticks $30.00-35.00
Cambridge "Lorna" vase, gold etching, 1930's $60.00-65.00
Duncan Miller "Three Leaf" sweet dip, 1920's $18.00-20.00
Fenton Swan candlesticks, 1938 . . . . $50.00-55.00
Fenton Elephant planter, 1928 . . . . $220.00-225.00
Fostoria "Mayfair" cup and saucer, 1930's $10.00-12.00
Fostoria "Fairfax" cream & sugar, 1930's $15.00-18.00
Greensburg Elephant ashtray, 1930's $13.00-15.00
Hazel Atlas "Floral Sterling" sherbet and plate $5.00-7.00
Hobbs "Windmere's Fan" sugar with

A black glass elephant flower bowl. This example from about 1928 is Fenton glass and worth about $200.00-225.00.

McKee "Tom & Jerry" set with silver writing from the 1930's is worth $70.00-75.00.

lid, 1890's $65.00-70.00
Imperial "Diamond Quilted" sherbet,
  1930's $3.00-4.00
Lancaster handled tray, 9½ ",
  1930's $4.00-6.00
McKee "Autumn" candlesticks, pair,
  4 ", 1930's $15.00-20.00
New Martinsville "Queen Anne"
  perfume bottle,
  1930's $15.00-18.00
Paden City "Peacock and Rose" vase,
  10 ", 1920's $45.00-50.00
L.E. Smith fernbowl with flower frog,
  1930's $10.00-12.00
L.E. Smith "Lace Renaissance"
  footed bowl, 1930 . . . $20.00-25.00
U.S. Glass 10 "vase, pink & gold
  flower design,
  1930's $15.00-18.00
Westmoreland "Chicken Sherbet",
  1930's $16.00-18.00
Hen on nest covered dish,
  white head $100.00-125.00

Blue and White Pottery

Blue and white pottery or crockery is sometimes called blue and grey crockery, salt glaze, or blue and grey pottery. The blue and white crockery pitchers, salt holders, bowls and miscellaneous pieces were very popular in the United States from the late 1800's into the 1930's. Though there are some stencilled designs, most decoration is in the form of embossings. Prices are climbing upward on this collectible.

Pitchers

Butterfly in circle . . . $150.00-175.00
Bluebird, 3 birds in
  flight $175.00-200.00
Flying bird $250.00-275.00
Peacock $250.00-300.00
Lovebirds, 2 birds in

circle $175.00-250.00
Swan in circle $135.00-175.00
Doe and fawn $150.00-175.00
Leaping deer $135.00-150.00
Cows drinking in
  circle $150.00-175.00
Cherry cluster, waffle
  back $150.00-175.00
Cherry cluster, basketweave
  back $135.00-150.00
Apricot $135.00-150.00
Cherries & leaves, blank
  midsection $150.00-175.00
Grape with leaf band, waffle
  back $115.00-125.00
Grape cluster on
  trellis $75.00-125.00
Grape cluster in
  shield $150.00-175.00
Wild rose $125.00-150.00
Basketweave and
  flower $150.00-175.00
Stenciled wildflower . $150.00-175.00
Daisy cluster,
  bulbous $150.00-175.00
Poinsettia, woven cane
  back $150.00-175.00
Iris $135.00-150.00
Old fashioned garden
  rose $125.00-150.00

Wesson Oil Jar. This jar was used as a beater jar and is valued at $50.00-65.00.

Cattails pitchers. Each is worth about $100.00-150.00.

The pitcher on the left is a Grape Cluster in Shield and worth $150.00-175.00. The Wild Rose pitcher on the right is valued at $125.00-150.00.

Tulip $125.00-135.00
American Beauty
    rose $200.00-225.00
Pine cone $150.00-175.00

Cattails $125.00-150.00
Windmill & bush $150.00-200.00
Avenue of trees $150.00-175.00
Stenciled acorn $100.00-135.00

40

An Apricots with Honeycomb butter crock with bail handle. $150.00-175.00.

The Butterfly salt on the left is worth $100.00-125.00. The Apricot salt on the right would bring $100.00-125.00 as well.

Dutch boy and girl . . $125.00-150.00
Swastika $165.00-185.00
Indian in circle $180.00-200.00
Lincoln $175.00-200.00
Castle & fish scale . . . $150.00-175.00

Salts

Apricots $100.00-110.00
Flying bird, with lid . $250.00-300.00
Eagle, with lid $225.00-275.00
Butterfly $100.00-125.00

Roaster. $150.00-175.00.

Heart and Drapery roaster without lid, $125.00-150.00. Add $40.00-50.00 for the lid.

Two sides of a Flying Bird salt. $250.00-300.00.

Blackberry $100.00-125.00
Blue band $75.00-95.00
Grapevine on fence ..$150.00-175.00
Daisy on snowflakes,
    with lid $150.00-175.00
"Salt" on waffle
    back $115.00-135.00
Love bird $115.00-135.00

Butters

Grapes & leaves $75.00-100.00
Butterfly, with bail ...$95.00-100.00
Cows and fence $200.00-300.00
Eagle, with bail $250.00-300.00
Apricots and honey-
    comb $150.00-175.00
Daisy and trellis....$100.00-125.00
Dragonfly and
    flower $150.00-175.00
"Butter" in scroll,
    with bail $95.00-125.00
Swastika $75.00-85.00
Blue stripe $95.00-115.00

Bowls

Rings Around, set of 5
    graduated sizes....$325.00-350.00
Feathers...........$100.00-125.00
Currents and

diamonds $75.00-100.00
Wildflower $65.00-75.00
Flying bird $85.00-95.00
Milk crock, lovebirds,
    with bail $100.00-125.00
Daisy & lattice $95.00-110.00

Miscellaneous

Water cooler, apple
    blossom ....$500.00+
Water cooler, Cupid .$475.00-525.00
Tea cooler, "Maxwell
    House" $175.00-200.00
Wesson Oil jar, 5″ tall .$50.00-60.00
Mug, flying bird $95.00-100.00
Toothbrush holder, blue
    band..............$35.00-45.00
Chamber pot,
    bowknot $125.00-145.00
Rolling pin, swirl....$200.00-225.00
Double roaster, chain
    link..............$100.00-125.00
Measuring cup, spearpoint
    flower panels $110.00-115.00

Blue Ridge

Southern Potteries' Blue Ridge Dinnerware is made up of a combination
of pattern shapes and pattern decora-

Blue Ridge tea pots. Back row left to right: "Mickey" on Colonial shape; "Windflower" on Colonial shape. Front row, left to right: "Rose Boquet" china; "Emalee" demi-pot; "Grape Wine" china. Each is worth $10.00-15.00.

Blue Ridge Toby mugs.

tion designs. Most collectible Blue Ridge consists of the dinnerware and accessories.

Chocolate pot with
  pedestal $20.00-30.00
Shakers, mallards $6.00-8.00
Character jug, Daniel
  Boone $40.00-50.00
Character jug,
  Indian $40.00-50.00
Platter, turkey, artist
  signed $40.00-55.00
Cereal bowl, 6″ $3.00-4.00
Bowl, open
  vegetable $5.00-10.00
Candy box, covered,
  6″ $12.00-15.00
Butter pat $1.00-3.00
Cake lifter $4.00-8.00
Child's bowl $5.00-8.00
Child's plate $3.00-5.00
Coffee pot $8.00-14.00
Demi pot $6.00-8.00
Casserole dish $3.00-5.00
Double egg cup $2.00-4.00
Cake plate, 10½″ $3.00-5.00
Covered sugar $3.00-7.00
Tidbit, two tier $6.00-9.00
Vase, ruffled top $15.00-20.00

Bottles

Bottles hold a fascination for many collectors. The first were crude containers holding whiskey, bitters, and other liquids. Gradually, improvements were made in the manufacturing processes of bottles and sealing methods. Liquor bottles, flasks, medicine bottles, soda bottles, beer bottles, and ink bottles are generally the most collected. The collector should be on the lookout for reproduction and re-issue bottles.

Dr. Caldwell Syrup Pepsin,
  medicine $1.00-2.00
Allen's Lung Balm, aqua,
  medicine $6.00-10.00
Ayer's Hair Vigor, green,
  medicine $10.00-20.00
Bauer's Instant Cough Cure,
  medicine $8.00-15.00
Block's German Bitters, amber,
  medicine $25.00-50.00

Bottles. Doyles Hop Bitters, $40.00-80.00; Electric Brand Bitters, $15.00-23.00.

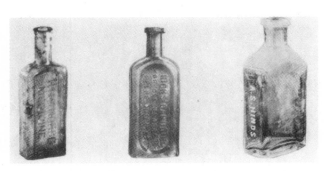

Medicine bottles, left to right: H.H.H. Celebrated Horse Medicine, $4.00-6.00; Hick's Capudine for Headaches, $2.00-4.00; A.S. Hinds, $1.00-2.00.

The bottle at left is a Garrett & Co., $2.00-3.00; the others are Mary T. Goldman bottles and are worth $4.00-6.00.

Crescent Drug Co., 7" clear,
  medicine $2.00-3.00
Father John's Medicine,
  7½ " $3.00-6.00
Johnson's Chill and Fever Tonic,
  clear, 6" medicine $2.00-3.00
Porter's Pain Killer, clear,
  6½ ", medicine $4.00-10.00
Thompson's Eye Water, 3¾ ",
  clear $3.00-5.00
Casino Queen Olives, clear,
  food $5.00-10.00
Elephant figure, Grapette,
  food $5.00-10.00
Mellin's Instant Food, green,
  food $3.00-5.00
O.K. Sweet Pickles, clear,
  food $5.00-7.00
Spack's Horseradish, aqua,
  food $3.00-5.00

Acorn Bitters, square,
  amber $60.00-80.00
Boxter's Mandrake Bitters,
  aqua $15.00-25.00
Berring Bitters, brown .. $5.00-10.00
Higby Tonic Bitters ... $15.00-25.00
Reed's Bitters, amber $115.00-125.00
Adam's Spring Mineral
  Water $3.00-5.00
Bacon's Soda Works, Sonora,
  CA, 7" $5.00-10.00
Bethesda Water, 12"..... $2.00-3.00
Lub's, Henry & Co., Savannah,
  GA, soda $10.00-15.00
Pacific Congress Water,
  7", soda $8.00-10.00
Poison, embossed rat,
  6½ " $4.00-8.00
Skull, figural, cobalt,
  poison $100.00-150.00

Dick's Ant Destroyer, clear,
   poison $15.00-25.00
Poison Tinct Iodine, skull
   & crossbones $4.00-6.00
Tri-Seps, skull & crossbones on
   label, poison $8.00-10.00

Boxes

Boxes of wood, cardboard, and other materials are plentiful and though there are exceptions, many can be bought very reasonably. Look for Shaker boxes, small wood boxes and product containers.

Document box, 12"x5", pine,
   1850's $150.00-175.00
Writing box, 10", pine &
   poplar $100.00-125.00
File card box, oak $25.00-50.00
Quaker Oats, wood, paper label,
   1900's $25.00-30.00
Dizzy Dean wrist watch box,
   heavy paper $20.00-25.00
Ballot box, walnut, slot in top,
   padlock, 1800's . . . $150.00-175.00
Kellogg's Wheat Krispies, sample box,

A wooden shipping box for Merry War Powdered Lye. $15.00-30.00.

   1930's $25.00-30.00
Bible box, hand carved walnut,
   1700's . . . . $200.00+
Quick Quaker Oats, paper,
   cylindrical $10.00-12.00
Candle box, handing,
   covered $175.00-200.00
Men's jewelry box, oak, drawer and
   hinged lid, brass
   nameplate $50.00-75.00
Velvet Starch, 1920's . . $10.00-12.00
Chalk box, wood, sliding
   lid $10.00-20.00
Royal Pudding with Howdy

A wood tobacco box, opticals box and cylindrical boxes.

This wooden box contained slat fish. $5.00-7.00.

Doody card, 1950's $5.00-7.50
Tramp art trinket box,
6¼ " $40.00-50.00

Boy Scouts & Scouting

The Boy Scout has been a symbol of honesty and morality in this country for a number of years. The many items produced for and about Scouts and Scouting are finding their way into col-lector's eager hands these days with some considerably valuable. Look for Rockwell art on some pieces.

Tin drum, 1907 .... $30.00-40.00
Equipment & Accessories
   Catalog, 1927 .... $20.00-30.00
First Aid Kit, 1940's ... $10.00-12.00
Girl Scout Handbook,
   1930's $5.00-10.00

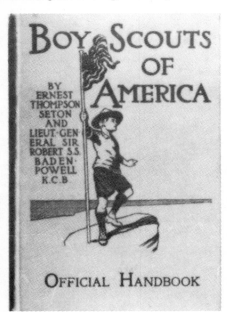

Two Boy Scout books from the early 1900's. The handbook at left is from 1913-14 and could bring as much as $45.00 or more. The camping book by Edward Cave is also from 1914 and worth about $25.00.

Coleman stove in canvas
case $10.00-12.00
Pinback button, boy scout with
bugle $5.00-7.00
Compass, 1940's $8.00-10.00
Membership cards, 1930's or
40's $2.50-4.00
Boy Scout handbook,
1930 ....$10.00-15.00
Jamboree neckerchief,
1930's $30.00-35.00
Uniform, 1920's $10.00-15.00
Boys Life magazine,
1930's $2.00-3.00
Calendar with Rockwell
art $10.00-20.00
Scoutmaster handbook,
1950's $2.00-5.00
Jamboree patch, 1957....$3.00-5.00
Catalog, *Scouting Christmas*,
1940's $3.00-5.00
Sleeping bag sales sheet,
1940's $2.00-3.00

Butter Molds

Butter molds or butter prints are round, rectangular, or square forms for molding and imprinting designs on butter. Though most are made of wood, some can be found in metal, glass, or other materials. The most common impressions on the molds are wheat, acorns, pineapples, and some floral designs. Most any animal impression is considered valuable, especially cows or deer. Beware of reproduction butter molds that are sometimes difficult to determine from the originals.

Wildflower $45.00-55.00
Daisy $40.00-50.00
Triple wildflower $40.00-50.00
Pennyslvania Tulip ...$85.00-115.00
Fern $40.00-50.00
Dandelion $40.00-50.00
Thistle $55.00-70.00

This Rose buttermold is hand-carved and about 3½″ in diameter. $30.00-35.00.

A Triple Wildflower buttermold. $35.00-40.00.

Animal molds are popular with collectors. This swan is about 3″ across and worth $50.00-60.00.

Sunflower	$40.00-50.00
Tulip	$90.00-120.00
Sheaf of wheat, octogonal	$300.00 +
Double acorn & leaves	$40.00-50.00
Cherry	$50.00-60.00
Pine twigs	$35.00-45.00
Pine cone & leaf	$85.00-100.00
Cow	$175.00-200.00
Eagle	$200.00-225.00
Sheep	$175.00-200.00
Rabbit	$150.00-175.00
Rooster	$150.00-175.00
Beaver	$75.00-100.00

Campaign Buttons

The first pinback buttons were used in the election of 1896. Their popularity has continued and they are still an effective means of candidate advertisement today. Early buttons were colorful, followed by a trend in the 30's and 40's toward red, white and blue. During this period most of the candidates buttons were very similar. In later years, the trend seems to be going back to more colorful buttons once again. The most popular buttons are jugates, buttons that feature both the presidential and vice presidential candidates. The collector should be very careful in purchasing political buttons. Many reproductions, especially of the earlier and more valuable buttons, are floating around.

(Photo courtesy of Hake's Americana & Collectibles)
A group of political buttons from World War II to 1972. Top row from left: Roosevelt, 1944, $10.00; Dewey, 1944, $9.00; Truman, 1948, $15.00; Dewey, 1948, $9.00; Eisenhower, 1952, $9.00; Stevenson, 1952, $9.00; Second row from left: Eisenhower, 1956, $5.00; Stevenson, 1956, $4.00; Kennedy, 1960, $7.50; Nixon and Lodge 1960 jugate, $7.00; Johnson, 1964, $5.00; Goldwater, 1964, $4.00; Bottom row from left: Nixon, 1968, $3.00; Humphrey and Muskie, 1968, $3.00; Wallace, 1968, $2.00; Nixon, 1972, $3.00; McGovern and Shriver, 1972, $2.00; McGovern and Eagleton, 1972, $4.00.

(Photo courtesy of Hake's Americana & Collectibles)

A group of early political pinback buttons. Top row from left: McKinley 1896, $15.00; Bryan, 1896, $15.00; McKinley and Roosevelt jugate, 1900, $25.00; Bryan and Stevenson jugate, 1900, $30.00; Roosevelt and Fairbanks jugate, 1904, $25.00; Parker and Davis jugate, 1904, $20.00. Second row from left: Taft, 1908, $12.00; Bryan, 1908, $15.00; Wilson and Marshall jugate, 1912, $35.00; Taft and Sherman jugate, 1912, $40.00; Roosevelt (Bull Moose), 1912, $15.00; Wilson and Marshall jugate, 1916, $35.00; Hughes, 1916, $25.00. Third row from left: Harding, 1920, $20.00; Cox and Roosevelt, 1920, $35.00; Coolidge, 1924, $30.00; La Follette and Wheeler, 1924, $15.00; Hoover, 1928, $25.00; Smith, 1928, $25.00. Bottom row from left: Roosevelt, 1932, $15.00; Hoover, 1932, $12.00; Roosevelt and Garner jugate, 1936, $12.00; Landon, 1936, $25.00; Roosevelt, 1940, $10.00; Willkie, 1940, $9.00.

Roosevelt-Fairbanks, jugate, 1904 . . . .$20.00-25.00	Wilson-Marshall, jugate, 1916 . . . .$35.00-40.00
Taft-Sherman, jugate, 1912 . . . .$35.00-45.00	Harding-Coolidge, red, white & blue, 1920 . . . .$30.00-35.00
Roosevelt, "Progressive" moose, 1912 . . . .$15.00-20.00	Coolidge, "Keep Coolidge", 1924 . . . .$10.00-12.00

52

Hoover, red, white & blue,
1928 . . . . $4.00-6.00
Landon, face in flower,
1936 . . . . $15.00-20.00
Roosevelt-Truman, tab back,
1944 . . . . $5.00-10.00
Dewey, "Elect Dewey, Warrren in
'48'', tab back $3.00-5.00
Truman, "Vote Truman and Barkley
in '48'' $15.00-20.00
Eisenhower, "I Like Ike",
1952 . . . . $2.00-3.00
Nixon-Lodge, jugate,
1960 . . . . $5.00-7.00
Kennedy, "For President", red, white,
& blue, 1960 . . . . $5.00-7.00
Humphrey-Muskie, jugate,
1968 . . . . $3.00-5.00
Nixon-Agnew, blue, red,
1972 . . . . $3.00-4.00
McGovern, peace sign,
1972 . . . . $1.00-2.00
McGovern-Eagleton,
1972 . . . . $3.00-5.00
Carter-Mondale, green & white,
1976 . . . . $1.00-3.00
Ford-Dole, "Look at the Record",
1976 . . . . $1.00-3.00

Campaign Collectibles

Campaign collectibles are popular "go withs" for political button collections, and more recently in their own right as collectibles. The historical value combined with the wide variety of collectibles available make this collecting hobby one that offers many opportunities. Anything used as a campaign item is considered collectible, especially material from early campaigns. Be cautious in buying political collectibles to avoid reproductions on the market.

Harrison, handkerchief, red, white &
blue, 1888 . . . . $40.00-55.00
Truman, mechanical pencil,
1948 . . . . $10.00-12.00
Nixon, poster, color,
1972 . . . . $3.00-5.00
Humphrey, bubble gum cigars, "Win
with HHH", in box . $20.00-25.00
Johnson (Lyndon), ceramic cowboy
hat $10.00-12.00
Harding-Coolidge, poster, oval
portraits, 1920 . . . . . $75.00-100.00
Alf Landon, paper napkins,
1936 . . . . $8.00-10.00

Campaign material from 1972.

Nixon, bumper sticker,
 1960 ....$7.00-10.00
Dewey, pennant, elephant,
 1948 ....$15.00-20.00
Coolidge-Dawes, window
 sticker $10.00-15.00
Taft, Inaugural medal, bronze in
 box, 1909 ....$250.00-275.00
Truman, poster, color,
 26"x32" $40.00-50.00
Eisenhower-Nixon, Inauguration
 program, 1953 ......$15.00-20.00
Lincoln-Hamlin, ribbon, "Union &
 Victory" $300.00-325.00
Kennedy, imitation straw hat,
 1960 ....$10.00-12.00
Bryan-Kern, watch fob,
 1908 ....$25.00-35.00
Grant, cane with head handle,
 1868 ....$125.00-175.00
Goldwater, "Au H$_2$O", 1964,
 license plate $10.00-12.00
Roosevelt, (F.D.R.), fan, heart
 shape $25.00-30.00
Eisenhower, cigarette lighter,
 1956 ....$15.00-25.00

Candy Containers

Figural containers of glass first became popular in the 19th century. The idea was to boost the sale of candy by packaging it in a container that could later be used as a toy. This was so successful that many manufacturers adopted the idea in the years following and packaged many products in the attractive containers. The collector should beware because some of the figural containers are still being produced or are currently being reproduced.

Firetruck, 5" $25.00-30.00
Sitting dog, 4".......$15.00-20.00
Tank, 4" $20.00-25.00
Locomotive..........$60.00-75.00
Rabbit with carrot.....$20.00-25.00
Santa $50.00-75.00
Bus...............$100.00-135.00
Mantel clock $100.00-115.00
Charlie Chaplin $100.00-125.00
Airplane, 4".........$10.00-20.00
Turkey, 3" $50.00-75.00

Glass candy containers. From left to right: McArthur hat $30.00-35.00; telephone $35.00-40.00; milk bottles in a wire rack $20.00-30.00.

Dog $5.00-10.00
Rabbit and
    wheelbarrow $100.00-125.00
Boot, 2½ " $10.00-15.00
Lantern, 3 " $10.00-15.00

Carnival Glass

Carnival Glass was originally called Taffeta, but because it was a popular give-away at carnivals, it came to be called Carnival Glass. Large quantities were produced from about 1900 to the 1930's but some manufacturers are still manufacturing the popular glassware. Carnival Glass is an iridized glass that has a "rainbow" effect when under sunlight. Many patterns were produced in several colors and many pieces are signed. The most poular makers of Carnival Glass were Millersburg, Northwood, and Fenton. The collector should be very cautious when buying Carnival Glass because many pieces are being made today.

Age Herald, plate,
    10 " .... $800.00+
Apple Blossom, bowl,
    7½ " $25.00-50.00
Balloons, compote $50.00-85.00
Basketweave,
    hat shape $30.00-40.00

Snow Fancy cream and sugar. $45.00 each.

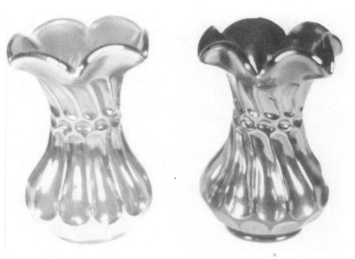

Thumbprint and Oval vases. The marigold example on the left is worth about $165.00, the dark version on the right is valued at $135.00.

Windmill pitcher. $65.00-155.00.

A pair of Premium candlesticks worth about $60.00-90.00.

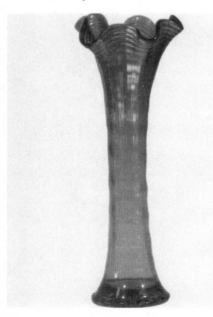

This Ripple carnival glass vase is worth $25.00-40.00.

Blackberry Spray,
   bon bon $30.00-40.00
Cane and Scroll,
   creamer $40.00-45.00

Cherry Chain, plate,
   7 " $80.00-125.00
Daisy, bon bon $45.00-55.00
Daisy Chain, shade $40.00-45.00
Elegance, bowl $85.00-100.00
Fanciful, plate, 9 " . . . $110.00-160.00
Feather Stitch bowl $50.00-75.00
Garland, footed rosebowl $45.00-65.00
Golden Grapes, bowl,
   7 " $35.00-45.00
Harvest Poppy,
   compote $40.00-60.00
Hearts & Flowers, bowl,
   8½ " $35.00-70.00
Iris, goblet $50.00-65.00
Jewels, vase $90.00-170.00
Kingfisher, bowl, 5 " . . . $40.00-50.00
Lattice, bowl $55.00-80.00
Malaga, bowl, 9 " $70.00-90.00
Northern Star,
   card tray $30.00-35.00
Open Rose, fruit bowl,
   10 " $30.00-50.00
Peacock, bowl, 5 " $40.00-50.00

Question Marks, cake
  plate . . . . $350.00 +
Rambler Rose,
  tumbler $25.00-35.00
Seagulls, bowl $80.00-90.00
Target, vase $30.00-60.00
Utility, lamp, 8″ $70.00-80.00
Valentine, ring tray $70.00-80.00
Vintage, compote $35.00-45.00
War Dance, compote . . $60.00-65.00
Wild Rose, bowl, flat,
  8″ $30.00-40.00
Woodpecker, wall vase . $40.00-80.00
Zig Zag, pitcher $200.00-300.00

Catalogs

One of the most popular sales aids in
this country for many years has been
the trade catalog. Through the collecting of these catalogs, the collector can
witness the types of things bought by
the American public over the years.
Some catalog collectors specialize in a
particular company and try to ac-
cumulate catalogs for that company
only. Others "zero in" on a specific
type of mechandise. Still others colect
a complete cross-section of many companies for many years. At any rate,

**Jewelry catalogs are good sellers. This ex-
ample is from Weiller and Son, 1917 and
is valued at $15.00-25.00.**

catalog collecting is growing as more
and more collectors "discover" these
collectibles. Be very careful in this
area, because many of the old trade
catalogs are being reproduced.

Appliances

Alaska Refrigerator Co., 24 pages,
  1911 . . . . $12.00-15.00
Allen Mfg. Co., ranges, 20 pages,
  1915 . . . . $5.00-7.00
Imperial Ranges, 49 pages,
  1920 . . . . $3.00-5.00
Richmond Cedar Works, washing
  machines, 16 pages,
  1905 . . . . $2.00-3.00
Western Electric, home appliances,
  16 pages, 1930 . . . . $3.00-5.00

China/Glassware

Burley & Co., 102 pages,
  1909 . . . . $65.00-70.00
Fostoria, 80 pages,
  1966 . . . . $25.00-30.00
Imperial Glass Co., Candlewick,
  25 pages, 1950 . . . . . . $15.00-25.00

**This D.M. Ferry seed catalog from the mid
1880's is worth about $15.00-20.00.**

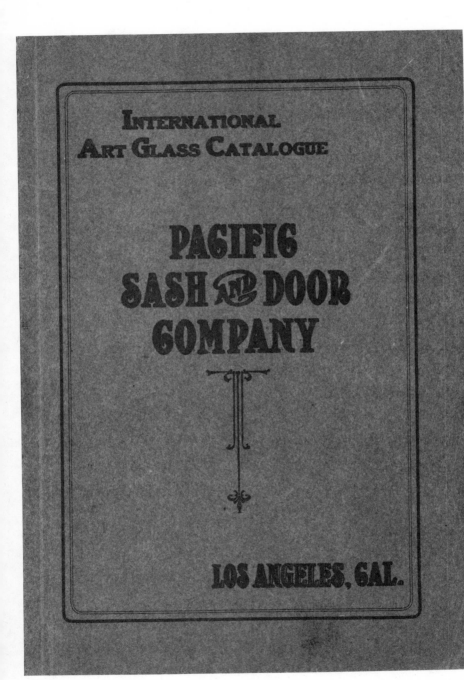

INTERNATIONAL
ART GLASS CATALOGUE

PACIFIC
SASH AND DOOR
COMPANY

LOS ANGELES, CAL.

Pacific Sash and Door Co. catalog featuring stained glass windows from the early 1900's.

Spear & Company general merchandise catalog from 1927.

Homer Laughlin, Fiesta,
   1938 . . . . $30.00-40.00
George Lefton, 24 pages,
   1940 . . . . $50.00-60.00

Farm

S.L. Allen, 56 pages,
   1908 . . . . $5.00-10.00
Bradley & Co., 20 pages,
   1890 . . . . $10.00-12.00
Craine Inc., 24 pages,
   1930 . . . . $3.00-5.00
Haworth & Sons, 8 pages,
   1890's $3.00-5.00
John Deere & Co., 16 pages,
   1912 . . . . $10.00-12.00

Furniture

C.W. Bent Co., 108 pages,
   1912 . . . . $25.00-30.00
F. Debski Inc., 32 pages,
   1930 . . . . $10.00-12.00
Fred Macy Co., 48 pages,
   1890 . . . . $15.00-20.00
E. O'Toole Co., 144 pages,
   1952 . . . . $4.00-6.00
Spear & Co., 140 pages,
   1930 . . . . $5.00-7.00

General

Bulter Bros., 1937 . . . . . $25.00-35.00
Larkin, Spring/Summer,
   1922 . . . . $20.00-30.00
Montgomery Ward, #92,
   1920 . . . . $40.00-45.00
Montgomery Ward, #113,
   Fall/Winter, 1930 . . . $35.00-40.00
J.C. Penney, Spring/Summer,
   1939 . . . . $12.00-15.00
Sears Roebuck & Co., #133,
   1916 . . . . $65.00-70.00
Sears Roebuck & Co., Fall/Winter,
   1921 . . . . $30.00-40.00
Spiegel, Spring/Summer,
   1943 . . . . $10.00-15.00

Character Collectibles

The popularity of comic characters and movie, radio, and T.V. characters has produced an onslaught of toys, games, books, lamps, dishes, and hundreds of other types of memorabilia. Anything named after the character, featuring his likeness, or remotely connected to the character is considered collectible. Most sought after items are those produced from the 1920's to the early 1950's, but some items of more recent production are becoming increasingly valuable. Early items of still popular characters generally are the most valuable.

Joe Palooka, doll, wood,
   jointed $40.00-50.00
Betty Boop, doll, 9½'',
   1930's $15.00-25.00
Woody Woodpecker, hand puppet,
   rubber & cloth, 1962 . . $5.00-7.00
Popeye & Olive Oyl, masks, paper,
   1940's . . . . $3.00-5.00- each
Henry, squeeze toy, 9½'',
   1950's $5.00-10.00
Felix The Cat, Schoenhut toy, wood
   & plastic, 4'',1920's . . $40.00-45.00
Dagwood, marionette, wood &
   plastic, 15'', 1940's . . $10.00-15.00
Captain Marvel, watch,
   1940's $150.00-175.00
Joe Palooka, lunch box, tin,
   1940's $45.00-50.00
Howdy Doody, Ovaltine
   mug $18.00-25.00
Orphan Annie, Ovaltine shaker,
   1930's $35.00-45.00
Charlie McCarthy, tin walking toy,
   1930's $175.00-190.00
Moon Mullins and Kayo, hand car,
   tin toy, 1940's $180.00-225.00
Dick Tracy, water pistol,
   1950's $5.00-10.00

Woody Woodpecker, 6½″ rubber figure is worth about $4.00-8.00.

This rubber Mighty Mouse figure was issued in the late 1950's or early 1960's and can be found for about $6.00-12.00.

Dick Tracy's Handcuffs for Junior. $10.00-15.00.

Mortimer Snerd, Jack-in-the-box,
1930's $35.00-45.00
Wimpy, marionette, 5″
1940's $30.00-40.00
Buck Rogers, Super Sonic Glasses,
1950's $25.00-35.00
Flash Gordon, Rocket Fighter,

A Herman Munster cloth and vinyl doll from the television show of the early 1960's "The Munsters", $15.00-20.00.

tin toy, 1930's $275.00-325.00
Happy Hooligan,
roly-poly $25.00-35.00
Yogi Bear, rubber squeeze toy,
1960's $3.00-5.00
Beetle Baily, vinyl figure,
3″ $3.00-5.00
Batman Utility Belt,
1940's $50.00-65.00
Tarzan Jungle map,
1930's $50.00-75.00
Sky King, plastic figures, Nabisco
premiums, 1950's, set . $8.00-10.00
Captain Video, flying Saucer
ring $15.00-20.00

Clocks

Clock collecting has been a major pastime of collectors for a number of years. There are many variations of clocks: wall clocks, mantel clocks, kitchen clocks, novelty clocks, grandfather clocks. Most popular with col-

A Seth Thomas shelf clock, 23½″ tall. This clock is worth about $185.

A German-made cottage clock, about 12″ tall, $130.00.

lectors are clocks made by the large clock companies: Seth Thomas, Waterbury, Ithaca, Ingraham, Welch,

Sessions, and Ansonia are only a few. Prices here are for clocks that have been completely restored and in good working condition.

Seth Thomas, Cambridge, mantel
1910 . . . . $130.00-150.00
Seth Thomas, Yale, mantel,
1910 . . . . $130.00-150.00
Seth Thomas, Bosnia, mantel,
1905 . . . . $85.00-100.00
Seth Thomas, O.G., weight,
1880's $90.00-100.00
Seth Thomas, St. Paul, spring,
1880's $175.00-200.00
Waterbury, #9091, kitchen,
1930's $180.00-200.00
Waterbury, Breton, wall,
1920's $200.00-225.00
Waterbury, Abner, novelty,
1918 . . . . $20.00-25.00
Waterbury, Dover, mantel,
1918 . . . . $75.00-100.00
Waterbury, Tornoto, Regulator,
1880's $400.00-500.00
Ansonia, Africa, mantel,
1880's $180.00-200.00
Ansonia, Cortez, mantel,
1880's $300.00-350.00
Ansonia, Reflector, wall,
1880's $500.00-600.00
New Haven, Mission Hanging, wall,
1918 . . . . $150.00-200.00
New Haven, Riverton, wall
1918 . . . . $200.00-225.00
New Haven, Camden, mantel,
1918 . . . . $160.00-175.00
New Haven, Erie, wall,
1918 . . . . $250.00-275.00
Howard, Norse, banjo,
1930's $175.00-200.00
Ingraham, Pekin, mantel,
1918 . . . . $75.00-85.00
Welch, #66, Cabinet,
1900 . . . . $125.00-150.00

Coca-Cola Collectibles

The success of Coca-Cola has provided American collectors with both a challenging and profitable hobby. Because of the extensive use of advertising Coca-Cola authorized production of great numbers of items to be given away as premiums and sold as promotion. Anything produced in the early 1900's is in great demand. Caution should be taken in this area because many of the more popular and valuable collectibles are being reproduced.

Bottle carton, cardboard,
   1930's $10.00-12.00
Bottle carton, wood,
   1920's $25.00-30.00
Radio, vending machine,
   1963 ....$60.00-65.00
Pencil sharpener, metal,

Tin thermometer from the early 1940's. $35.00-$45.00.

   1930's $5.00-7.00
Blotter, bottle, "Over 60 Million
   A Day", 1960's $2.00-3.00
Cards, ice skater,
   1950's $15.00-20.00
Ashtrays, heart, diamond, spade,
   club, all 4 ....$30.00-35.00
Ashtray with miniature bottle,
   1950's $50.00-60.00
Thermometer, tin, two bottles,
   1941 ....$50.00-60.00
Calendar, fishing boy,
   1937 ....$125.00-150.00
Blotter, Santa & kids,
   1938 ....$ 00-7.00
Mechanical pencil,,
   1930's $25.00-30.00
Jigsaw puzzle in can,
   1960's $15.00-20.00
Bottle, Japan, recent ..$10.00-20.00
Pencil box with contents,
   1930's $40.00-45.00

Coca-Cola cardboard standup of Santa Claus from the 1950's.

Sewing thimble, 1920's . $30.00-35.00
Door push, bottle-shaped,
    1950's $50.00-60.00
Pretzel dish, aluminum, 3 bottles
    hold bowl, 1930's ...$15.00-25.00
Cigarette lighter, bottle shape,
    plastic, 1950's $5.00-7.00
Bottle, large display,
    Dec. 25, 1923 ..... $100.00-125.00

Coca-Cola Trays

Trays, only one of many types of advertising items produced by Coca-Cola, continue to be very high on collector's want lists these days. The colorful attractive trays that have been in production since 1898 are demanding premium prices as more people begin to "discover" these images of American life. The changes in the characters and scenes on the trays reflect the changes in this country in fashion and social events. The prices here are for the large serving trays, rather than the small change trays that were generally small versions of the former. Be on the lookout for reproductions in this area because many are being sold today.

1898, round, girl with
    glass $4,000.00
1900, round, Coke bottle,
    5¢ .... $750.00 +
1900, round, Hilda Clark ...$600.00
1904, round, Hilda Clark .$500.00 +
1904, oval, St. Louis Fair and
    girl $200.00-300.00
1904, smaller version of
    above $175.00-200.00
1904, oval, Lillian Russell, glass
    on table .... $500.00 +
1904, same as above with bottle
    on table .... $500.00 +
1905, oval, girl drinking from
    glass $150.00-300.00

1927 Coke tray.

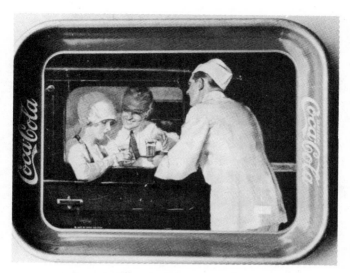

Another 1927 Coca-Cola tray.

1928 Coca-Cola tray.

1907, oval, girl holding
   glass $200.00-350.00
1908-1912, Topless girl, advertising
   on front . . . .$300.00+

1908-1912, same as above,
   advertising on
   back $100.00-150.00
1908-1912, Vienna Art, four

Pretty girls can frequently be found on Coke trays. This one is from 1932.

The 1933 Coke tray picturing Frances Dee.

different, advertising on
back $125.00
1909, oval, Coca-Cola
Girl .... $300.00+
1909, rectangle, same as
above .... $300.00+
1912, oval, girl with hat holding
glass $125.00-250.00
1912, rectangle, same as
above $125.00-200.00
1914, oval, "Betty" . $200.00-225.00
1917, long rectangle, girl with
roses holding glass . $85.00-100.00
1920, oval, girl in hat with
glass $175.00-250.00
1920, rectangle, same as
above $100.00-200.00
1921, rectangle, cloesup of girl in
hat holding glass . . $125.00-150.00
1922, rectangle, girl with small hat
under tree $250.00-300.00
1923, rectangle, girl in
shawl $100.00-125.00
1924, rectangle, girl with
glass $85.00-100.00
1925, rectangle, girl with fur and
hat holding glass $65.00-85.00
1926, rectangle, golfer pouring
Coke for girl $85.00-100.00
1927, rectangle, soda
jerk $75.00-100.00
1927, rectangle, car
hop.............. $125.00-175.00
1930, girl in swimsuit &
cap $65.00-75.00
1931, rectangle, "Tom
Sawyer" $100.00-200.00
1932, rectangle, girl in chair wearing
swimsuit $150.00-200.00
1933, rectangle, Frances
Dee................ $75.00-125.00
1934, rectangle, J. Weismuller &
M. O'Sullivan $175.00-250.00
1935, rectangle, Madge
Evans.............. $45.00-65.00

1936, rectangle, girl with long
gown on chair $50.00-75.00
1937, rectangle, girl in swimsuit
& cape running $50.00-75.00
1938, rectangle, girl in large
hat $40.00-50.00
1939, rectangle, girl in swimsuit on
diving board $35.00-50.00
1941, rectangle, girl in ice
skates $40.00-50.00
1942, rectangle, two girls and
car $40.00-50.00
1943, rectangle, girl with scarf
holding bottle $20.00-30.00
1950, rectangle, girl with hat
holding bottle $20.00-25.00
1956, rectangle with wavy edges,
party food $12.00-15.00

Coffee Mills

Coffee mills, or grinders, used to chop
coffee beans pre-date the current electric drip machines so popular today.
Once a necessity, these compact
devices went the way of the washboard
and apple peeler. Many are made of
wood and are usually table mills, lap
mills, or wall mills. Commercial
grinders are generally not as popular
as home models.

Table mill, wood,
Chas. Parker Co. ...$65.00-95.00
Table mill, wood, 1 lb. capacity,
"Brighton Coffee
Mill" $55.00-70.00
Table mill, wood,
Arcade $65.00-87.00
Primitive lap mill, wood, pewter
hopper, iron words . $90.00-130.00
Lap mill, iron works,
pine $75.00-85.00
Lap mill, wood,
Imperial............ $60.00-90.00
Lap mill, wood, iron top & hopper,

A primitive lap coffee mill made of walnut with dovetail joints and tin hopper. This example is valued at $100.00-$140.00.

Another primitive lap mill with a brass hopper. The wood is cherry with dovetail joints. $100.00-$135.00.

"Colonial" $35.00-50.00
Commercial mill, "Swift Mill - Lane Bros." $185.00-250.00
Commercial mill, "Enterprise Mfg. Co.", eagle on top $325.00-400.00

Canister mill, glass & iron, wall mount, "Crystal" . . . $45.00-55.00
Canister mill, wood & iron, "Arcade" $25.00-45.00
Canister mill, tin,

This lap mill has a cast iron top and poplar wood box. $50.00-$70.00.

An Arcade Crystal coffee mill. This wall mount style is worth about $35.00-$55.00.

"Grand Union" $65.00-85.00
Side mill, iron, "Baldwin
Sons Co." $25.00-50.00
Table mount mill,
"Universal" $25.00-45.00
Table or wall mount mill, cast iron,
"Enterprise" $25.00-45.00

Coin Operated Machines

If you drop coins in a slot and the machine goes into action, the gadget is probably now collectible. Any type is popular but leading the list are the old jukeboxes from the 1940's and 1950's. Outlandish in style and guady in design, these colorful, ornate pieces of Americana can demand thousands of dollars.

Jukebox, Rock-Ola
    1426 ....$1,200.00+
Jukebox, Wurlitzer
    1080 ....$3,000.00+
Jukebox, Rock-Ola

The classic of all jukeboxes. This Wurlitzer 1015 is from the 1940's and would bring about $4,000.00 on up for a machine in good condition.

1422 . . . . $1,200.00 +
Jukebox, Wurlitzer
  950 . . . . $5,000.00 +
Jukebox, Wurlitzer
  500 . . . . $1,000.00 +
Jukebox, Rock-Ola
  1428 . . . . $1,200.00 +
Mills "Punching Bag",
  1900's $1,200.00-1,500.00
Challenger "Duckshoot",
  1940's $175.00-200.00
Multoscope, "It's a Knockout",
  1940's . . . . $1,000.00 +
Flipper pinball, Gottlieb, "4 Belles",

1950's $400.00-500.00
Adams Gum Vendor,
  1940's $100.00-125.00
Candy vendor, "The Old Mill',
  1920's $625.00-750.00
Postage vendor, 1910 $275.00-350.00
Jukebox, Packard Manhattan,
  1940's . . . . $3,000.00 +
Jukebox, Seeburg, 100B,
  1950's $650.00-750.00
Mills "Wizard Fortune Teller",
  1920's $500.00-600.00
Zeno Gum Wendor,
  1910 . . . . $275.00-350.00

Advance Gumball,
1920's $150.00-175.00
Ohio Book Matches,
1950's $40.00-50.00
Bingo, 1930's $400.00-500.00

Collector Prints

Limited edition prints have become very popular with collectors in the past few years. Some signed and numbered limited edition prints, even though they are not old, bring considerably more than their original purchase prices. Prints by American artists Norman Rockwell, Charles Frace ', Ray Harm, and other noted wildlife artists are much in demand. Largely due to the limited production of these lithographs, the values appreciate rapidly on high quality prints. Prices here are for signed and numbered limited edition prints.

James Bama, "Mountain
Man" $250.00-300.00
Robert A. Christie, "Steady and
Stylish" $40.00-50.00
Guy Coheleach, "Golden
Eagle" $400.00-500.00
Jerry Crandle,
"Pursued" $50.00-75.00
Don Elkelberry, "Ruffled
Grouse" $85.00-100.00
Carl Evers, "Heavy
Seas" $60.00-70.00
Charles Frace ',
"Cougar" $325.00-375.00
Ray Harm,
"Mallard" $70.00-80.00
Ralph J. McDonald,
"The Champion" . $120.00-140.00
Bob McGinnis,
"Winter Wheat" $50.00-75.00
Charles Pearson,
"Autumn Geese" . . . $30.00-40.00

This signed and numbered print by Ralph McDonald is called 'The Champion' and is worth about $125.00.

"The Good Omen" by Bev Doolittle is worth about $75.00 for signed and numbered copies.

"Eastern Honkers" by Wayne Spradley is worth about $50.00.

Signed & numbered editions of Peter Darro's "Call of the Wild" are valued at $200.00.

The 'Catoosa Whitetail' by Dick Elliot is worth about $50.00 for signed and numbered editions.

Maynard Reece,
 "Bobwhites" $650.00-750.00
Tom Sanders,
 "Dawn Patrol" $60.00-80.00
Paul Sawyier, "River Friends"
 (numbered only) $25.00-35.00
Manfred Schatz,
 "Lynx" $75.00-100.00
John Schoenberr,
 "Clam Bar" $60.00-70.00
Tucker Smith,
 "Hay Shed" $175.00-200.00
J. Sharkey Thomas, "Cheetah and
 Cubs" $75.00-100.00
Richard Thompson,
 "Autumn Day" . . . $100.00-125.00
Richard Evans Younger,
 "Canada Geese" $60.00-70.00

Comic Books

Comics have become more and more popular especially as the publicity of the hobby has increased. Collectors of all ages have swarmed to this new collectible that was once the domain of the youngster, causing a demand for some early rare books. The most popular valuable issues of comic books are those from the "Golden Age" that lasted from 1930 until 1950, especially the well known comic characters. Collectors are always on the lookout for issues containing the first appearance of a popular character. Some of these early examples can bring hundreds or even thousands of dollars to the alert seller. Comic books containing the work of Disney artist Carl Barks have become very valuable in recent years. Though there are some very valuable comic books, most are still worth only a few cents each.

Action #1, 1st Superman,
 1938 . . . . $2,000+
Archie #1, .$1940's .$150.00-300.00
Beany and Cecil, 1952 . .$5.00-10.00
Beetle Bailey, 1950's . . . . .50¢-$1.50
Blondie & Dagwood,
 1960's $2.00-3.50
Bugs Bunny, 1943 . . . . . $30.00-65.00
Bugs Bunny (Puffed Rice),
 1940's $1.00-2.00
Captain Marvel Adventures #1,
 1941 . . . . $500.00+

Tarzan Comic, 1950's, $1.00-3.00.

Lone Ranger comic book from the 1950's. $1.00-3.00.

Zorro comic from 1957. $1.00-3.00.

Detective Comics, 1st
  Batman . . . . $1,000.00 +
Ellery Queen, 1949 . . . . $10.00-20.00
Frogman Comics, 1950's . $3.00-5.00
Gang Busters, 1930's-early
  1940's $10.00-20.00
Green Hornet #1,
  1940 . . . . $50.00-100.00
Howdy Doody #1,
  1949 . . . . $5.00-10.00
Jungle Girl, 1942 . . . . . $25.00-35.00
Jungle Jim, 1950's $1.50-3.50
Lassie #1, 1950 . . . . $3.00-5.00
Leave It To Beaver, late
  1950's $1.50-3.00
McHale's Navy,
  1960's . . . . 50¢-$2.00
Mighty Mouse #1,
  1946 . . . . $15.00-25.00
Nightmare #1,
  1952 . . . . $10.00-20.00
Pancho Villa, 1950's . . . $10.00-20.00
Piracy, 1950's . . . . . : . . $15.00-25.00
Ratfink, 1960's . . . . 50¢-$1.00
The Rifleman, 1959 . . . . $2.50-5.00
Sarge Steel, 1960's . . . . 50¢-$1.00
Star Trek #1,
  1967 . . . . $10.00-15.00
Sun Girl, 1940's $35.00-50.00
Teen Comics, 1940's $3.00-5.00
Texas John Salughter $1.00-2.00
T-Man #1, 1951 . . . . $7.00-15.00
True Love Confessions,
  1950's . . . . . . : $4.00-8.00
Voyage to the Bottom of the Sea,
  1961 . . . . $3.00-5.00
Yakky Doodle & Chopper,
  1960's . . . . 50¢-$1.00
Young Lover Romances,
  1950's . . . . 50¢-$1.00

Cowboy Collectibles

The heroes of millions of American
boys from the 1920's to the 1960's were
the cowboys of movies, radio shows,
and T.V. programs. These protectors
of the American way illustrated quite
clearly the difference between good
and bad and the rewards of a moral
life. The premiums and products bas-
ed on these characters are very popular
with many fetching high prices.

Roy Rogers and Trigger, Hartland
  figure, 1960's $12.00-18.00
Roy Rogers, Dale Evans & Bullet, toy
  jeep, from T.V.
  show $50.00-60.00
Hopalong Cassidy, doll, complete,
  21" $100.00-125.00
Lone Ranger, Big Little
  Books, each $15.00-25.00
Cisco Kid & Pancho, paper masks,
  1950's $3.00-5.00
Tom Mix, Sixgun Decoder,
  1940's $20.00-25.00
Smiley Burnette, autographed
  photo $5.00-10.00
Hopalong Cassidy, pocketknife,
  3½", 1940's $15.00-20.00
Roy Rogers, Double R Bar Ranch,

A Red Ryder Big Little Book. This example would be worth about $5.00 in its
condition.

Gene Autry and Roy Rogers pinback buttons, $10.00.

play set, buildings & figures, complete, 1950's $25.00-30.00
Wild Bill Hickock & Jingles, photo badge, 1960's $3.00-5.00
Red Ryder, target game, 1930's $20.00-25.00
Rin Tin Tin, ring, plastic, 1950's $2.00-3.50
Gene Autry, cap gun, 1940's $15.00-20.00
Hopalong Cassidy, board game, 1950's $12.00-15.00
Lone Ranger, card game, 1930's $10.00-15.00
Red Ryder, BB gun (Daisy) $25.00-35.00
Gene Autry, color book, Merrill, 1940's $15.00-25.00
Tom Mix, secret manual, 1940's $50.00-60.00
Roy Rogers, ring with branding iron, 1940's $20.00-25.00
Roy Rogers, pistol & spur set, 1940's $25.00-35.00

Crockery

Crockery, also known as stoneware, pottery, and earthenware is made of clay that has been baked and glazed. The advantage of this kind of container was largely that the crock could keep cold materials cool for a longer

period of time than glass bottles. Also, anything affected by light could be safely stored in the heavy opaque containers. The majority of pottery jars and jugs were made in the 1800's but many were produced more recently. Advertising crocks, crocks with a company's name or markings, are becoming very popular. The collector should

This jug is marked A. B. Wheeler and has a cobalt leaf design. It is valued at about $100.00.

A two-gallon crock with dog decoration. $165.00.

be careful because it is often difficult to determine new from old crockery. One method to distinguish the difference is to find "turkey tracks", hairline age cracks in the interior or exterior of the jug. These cracks can also be reproduced, however, so extreme caution should be taken. Crockery with interior glaze was not produced until this century.

2 gallon jug, painted bird, New York
  Stoneware, 1870's . $250.00-300.00
2 gallon jug, cobalt flower, "Lyons",
  1870's $175.00-225.00
6 gallon crock, bird design,
  1860's $300.00-375.00
1½ gallon pickling jar, flower design,
  1850's $150.00-175.00
4 gallon crock, bird design, "Hart,
  Ogdensburg",
  1850's $325.00-375.00
1½ gallon jar, star design,

1800's $100.00-150.00
Beer bottle, brown $30.00-35.00
Whiskey jug, plain $40.00-50.00
Milk bowl, redware . . $150.00-165.00
5 gallon churn, leaf and flower
  decoration $80.00-100.00
Apple butter jar, 6½ ",
  redware $25.00-35.00
Jar with lid, speckled brown glaze,
  10 " $165.00-175.00
½ gallon crock, feather
  design $55.00-65.00
Jar, salt glaze earthenware, plain,
  12 " $12.00-18.00
Cream crock, bail and wood
  handle $20.00-30.00
Mixing bowl, salt
  glaze $25.00-30.00
Jug, with pouring lip, "Geo.
  Augusts" $75.00-100.00
Crock, leaf design,
  "Troy" $125.00-150.00
4 gallon crock, rooster

decoration $325.00-350.00
2 gallon crock, shaking hands
decoration $50.00-65.00

Cut Glass

Cut glass is extremely popular among collectors, especially those pieces produced during the period known as the "Brilliant Age", 1875-1915. Cut glass has a high lead content making it ring when thumped lightly and also causing it to have considerable weight. It is glass that has been hand blown and hand decorated with an abrasive wheel. The edges on the indentations of cut glass are sharper than on pieces of pressed glass. Signed glass or those pieces with the company name or trademark are premium items and demand higher prices. The signature is made by a stamp that has been saturated with an acid solution. Prices here are for cut crystal in perfect condition. The collector should be especially careful of chips on cut glass and also reproduction glass that closely resembles the originals.

Pansy basket, Pitkins &
Brooks $320.00-350.00

Cut glass cologne bottle. $35.00-$45.00.

Tea bell, 5¾ " $140.00-150.00
Bon bon, Beverly, Pitkins &
Brooks $90.00-115.00
Venice salad bowl, Pitkins &
Brooks, 8 " $85.00-95.00
Victoria, candlesticks, 7 ",
Bergen $100.00-140.00
Progress, carafe, quart,
Bergen $140.00-170.00
Ruby, celery tray, Averbeck,
11¼ " $80.00-100.00
Seaside, cigar jar,
Bergen $170.00-195.00
Belmont, cologne, Pitkins &
Brooks $35.00-45.00
Prism, pomade jar,
Bergen $40.00-50.00

This cut glass water set is the Golf pattern and is valued at $160.00-$175.00.

J. D. Bergen covered butter and plate. $245.00-255.00.

Pitkins & Brooks bud vase, 10″ tall, $80.00-$90.00.

Cut glass goblet. $40.00-$60.00.

Split & Hollow, pin
tray $65.00-75.00
Heart, compote, Pitkins &
Brooks $180.00-195.00
Glenwood, cordial set,
Bergen $300.00-350.00
Belvedere, cream and sugar, Higgins
& Seiter $50.00-60.00
Vienna, cup,
Averbeck $30.00-40.00
Palace, cruet,
Bergen $60.00-75.00
Marie, decanter,
Bergen $330.00-385.00
Cut Star, goblet, Higgins &
Seiter $25.00-40.00
Amazon, ice tub,

This cut glass spooner is worth about $100.00 or more.

Bergen $200.00-225.00
Delta, pitcher, 1 pint,
   Bergen $110.00-125.00

Decoys

Decoys have been used for many years to lure waterfowl to hunting areas. The decoys are wood turned or hand carved models of the fowl, painted to resemble them and used to attract the birds into shooting range. The most valuable decoys are the early ones of wood, especially the more detailed. Prices can fluctuate due to quality of workmanship, condition and rarity. Beware of modern reproductions.

Goose, cork and wood, glass
   eyes $70.00-80.00
Golden Eye Merganser,
   wood $40.00-50.00
Green Wing Teal, hen,
   wood $45.00-50.00
Duck, wood, paint
   removed $25.00-35.00
Black Duck, wood . . . $85.00-120.00
Goose shadow on spike, wood,
   1940's $50.00-60.00
Widgeon, pine $175.00-200.00
Bluebill, hen, wood. . $125.00-165.00
Broadbill, drake,
   pine $130.00-175.00
Crow, hand carved . . . . . $1,00.00 +
Canvasback, drake,

Crow or raven decoy, $500.00 or more.

This Black Duck decoy is valued at $75.00-$100.00.

wood $50.00-60.00
Goldeneye, drake, wood, glass
   eyes $65.00-75.00
Goose, canvas covered,
   painted $100.00-125.00
Canada Goose, wood, glass eyes, hand
   carved. . . . . $250.00 +

Mallard, drake, wood, glass
   eyes $125.00-150.00
Mallard, hen, wood, glass
   eyes $120.00-140.00

Depression Glass

Depression glass is the glassware that

Princess. Candy dish, $32.00-35.00; plate, $10.00-15.00; tumbler, $15.00-22.00; cream and sugar, $14.00-16.00.

Victory. Gravy boat and platter, $95.00; plate, $9.00; cream and sugar, $15.00; cup and saucer, $7.00.

Aurora. Tumbler, $8.00; bowl, $5.00; plate, $3.00; bowl, $5.00; cup and saucer, $7.00.

Cameo, Ballerina. Footed tumbler, $10.00-20.00; plate, $8.00-13.00, candlesticks, $70.00 pair; sugar, $15.00-17.00; cup and saucer, $65.00-70.00.

Colonial Block. Butter dish, $25.00-30.00; bowl, $5.00-10.00; candy dish, $20.00-25.00; cream and sugar, $15.00.

Cube "Cubist". Powder jar, $10.00-15.00; plate, $3.00-5.00; cup and saucer, $5.00-10.00; candy dish, $20.00-25.00.

Doric. Tumbler, 25.00-35.00; plate, $8.00; sherbet, $8.00; cup and saucer, $8.00-10.00.

Floral Poinsettia. Cream and sugar, $16.00; plate, $10.00; sherbet plate, $3.50; tumbler, $10.00-13.00; sherbet, $8.00-9.50.

Fortune. Berry bowl, $2.50; bowl, $4.00; tumbler, $4.00; candy dish, $12.50.

Homespun, "Fine Rib". Cup and saucer, $6.00; platter, $8.50; cream and sugar, $13.00; child's covered tea pot, $50.00.

Lace Edge, "Open Lace". Tumbler, $35.00; cream and sugar, $26.00; salad plate, $11.50; candy dish, $32.50.

New Century. Cream and sugar, $10.50; plate, $9.50; sherbet, $5.00; ashtray, $25.00.

Adam. Cup & saucer, $16.00-18.00; cake plate, $10.00-15.00; plate $15.00; candlesticks, $45.00-65.00 pair; divided dish, $9.00.

Anniversary. Cream & sugar, $5.00-10.00; sherbet plate, $1.00-2.00; sherbet, $2.50-4.50; cup, $2.00-4.00.

Beaded Block. Plates, $5.00-10.00; pitcher, $117.50; stemmed jelly, $8.00-15.00.

Bowknot. Cup, $6.50; salad plate, $6.00; tumbler, $10.00; berry bowl, $8.00; sherbet $7.50.

Cherry Blossom. Cup & saucer, $18.00-20.00; plate, $12.00-15.00; sandwich tray, $12.00-15.00.

Christmas Candy. Cream & sugar, $13.00; luncheon plate, $5.00.

Circle. Bowl, $5.50; cup, $2.00; pitcher, $17.50; sherbet, $3.50; water goblet, $6.50; wine goblet, $4.00.

Coronation "Banded Fine Rib". Cup & saucer, $4.00-5.00; plate, $3.50-5.50; large berry bowl, $7.00-11.00; berry bowl, $3.00-4.50; tumbler, $7.50.

Cupid. Small sugar, $25.00; ice bucket, $47.50; sugar, $30.00; plate, $22.00.

Diana. Cream & sugar, $7.00; plate, $5.00; bread & butter, $1.50; cup, $4.00.

Doric & Pansy. Salt shaker, $385.00 (with pepper); salad plate, $27.50; berry bowl, $6.50; cup & saucer, $20.00.

Floragold "Louisa". Cream & sugar, $15.00; pitcher, $20.00; cup & saucer, $10.50; covered candy dish, $30.00.

Floral & Diamond Band. Covered butter dish, $77.50; luncheon plate, $12.00; tumbler, $10.00; sherbet, $4.50.

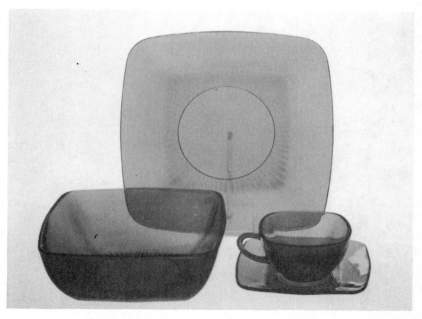

Forest Green. Salad bowl, $6.00; plate, $9.00; cup & saucer, $4.50.

Georgian Lovebirds. Sherbet, $8.50; vegetable bowl, $45.00; cream & sugar, $16.00-20.00; berry bowl, $5.00; plate, $6.00.

Hex Optic Honeycomb. Ice bucket, $8.00; salt & pepper, $17.50; tumbler, $5.50.

Laurel. Covered cheese, $50.00; sherbet, $7.00; candlesticks, $20.00-22.00 pair; vegetable bowl, $11.00-13.50; salad plate, $3.00-5.00.

Mayfair Open Rose. Creamer, $13.00-45.00; cake plate, $25.00-37.50; cup & saucer, $20.00-40.00; candy dish, $35.00-125.00. Blue Mayfair is worth considerably more than pink.

Moderntone Wedding Band. Creamer, $6.00-7.00; cup & saucer $7.00-9.00; luncheon plate, $5.00; salt & pepper, $22.50-27.50; sugar, $6.00-7.00.

Peacock & Wild Rose. Covered candy dish, $57.50; bowl with handle, $32.50; vase, $57.50; candlesticks, $37.50 pair.

was made during the years of the Depression, usually in pink, green, amber, blue, red, yellow, white and crystal. Most of the glassware can be found in pastel shades of translucent glass, and originally most was given away as premiums or sold at a very low price. Because so much of the glassware was produced, there are millions of pieces of Depression glass on the market and in private collections across the country. The collector should be very careful because reproduction Depression has been turning up around the country.

Disney Collectibles

Walt Disney created many characters that were immediately popular and manufacturers produced hundreds of different toys and likenesses of these. Mickey Mouse is by far the most popular, but Donald Duck, Snow White and the Seven Dwarfs, Pluto, Goofy, and many others follow close behind. Certain original Mickey Mouse watches bring $200.00-300.00, but there are several Mickey Mouse watches available, some being produced today. The most popular Disney items are those from the 1930's and 1940's.

Mickey Mouse, Globe Trotters map, 1930's $75.00-100.00
Donald Duck, rubber figure, 6″ $50.00-60.00
Mickey Mouse, doll, wood, "Borgfeldt", 7″ $100.00-150.00
Captain Hook, hand puppet $3.00-5.00
Mickey Mouse, drum, tin, 6″ $40.00-50.00
Donald Duck, pull toy, xylophone player.............. $20.00-25.00
Dopey, mask, 1930's $5.00-7.50
Seven Dwarfs, rubber figures, 1930's $80.00-115.00

This Minnie Mouse doll is 14½″tall and worth from $80.00 to 160.00. The Mickey Mouse doll on the right is from the 1930's and is 21″ high, $175.00-$350.00.

Donald Duck figure from the Sun Rubber Company. $12.00-$25.00.

This Dopey tin wind-up toy was made by Marx in the 1930's and can be found for $100.00-$200.00.

Donald Duck Xylophone player. $18.00-$36.00.

Mickey Mouse, figure, lead, 2½ ",

1930's $3.00-5.00
Mickey Mouse, piano, wood with
  decal, 1930's.......$75.00-100.00
Minnie Mouse, cloth doll,
  14½ "............$90.00-130.00
Mouseketeers hat,
  1950's $5.00-10.00
Pinocchio, doll, Ideal,
  8 "................$40.00-50.00
Pluto, wood, 1930's ...$18.00-25.00
Snow White & Seven Dwarfs, sewing
  set, Hasbro...........$4.00-5.00
Witch, mask............$5.00-7.00
Mickey & Donald's Race to Treasure
  Island, 1930's.......$25.00-35.00
Mickey Mouse Club, pinback,
  1920's $25.00-30.00
Pinocchio, bisque
  figure..............$25.00-35.00
Donald Duck, cookie
  jar $37.00-42.00
"Who's Afraid of the Big Bad
  Wolf?", sheet music,
  1930's $15.00-18.00
Dumbo, ceramic figure,
  6 "................$40.00-50.00

Dolls, Advertising

Many companies have offered dolls as premiums over the years. These dolls, advertising products and services, are available in a wide range of prices with some early scarce dolls bringing hundreds of dollars. Many can still be found in the $10.00-and-under range and some advertisers still offer dolls as premiums.

A&W Root Beer, bear, cloth,
  13 "................$3.00-5.00
American Beauty Macaroni, "Roni
  Mac", cloth,
  11 "...............$30.00-35.00
Arbuckle Bros. Coffee, "Jill", cloth,
  14½ ", 1931 ....$35.00-45.00

This Johnny doll is from the 1940's and was used to advertise Phillip Morris tobacco products. $65.00.

A 7½ "fisherman advertised Gorton's Codfish. He is vinyl and jointed at the head and shoulders. $8.00.

Chesty Potato Chips offered this Chesty Boy in the 1950's. He is an 8" squeak toy and worth about $10.00.

Fresh Up Freddie was offered by Seven-Up in the late 1950's. $25.00.

Aunt Jemima, cloth, 17",
    1924 . . . .$30.00-45.00
Babbit Cleanser, "Babbit Boy", composition and cloth, 15",
    1916 . . . .$200.00-225.00
Budweiser, "Bud Man", rubber,

    18" $15.00-20.00
Burger King, "King", cloth,
    1970's $2.00-3.00
Ceresota Flour, "Flour Boy", cloth,
    16", 1912 . . . .$175.00+
Chesty Potato Chips, "Chesty Boy",

rubber, 8", 1950's . . . $10.00-12.00
Chrysler, "Mr. Fleet", plastic bank,
10" $3.00-5.00
Derby Oil, gas station attendant, cloth,
17", 1960's $5.00-7.00
Dutch Boy, 12" puppet, vinyl & cloth,
1950's $8.00-10.00
Fisk Tires, Fisk Sleepy Boy, composition, 21" $85.00-100.00
General Electric, "Bandy", wood &
composition, 18",
1920's . . . . $300.00 +
Hawaiian Punch, "Punchy", cloth,
13", 1960's $8.00-10.00
Holland-American Lines, sailor,
12½", 1930's $25.00-30.00
Rice Krispies, "Crackle", cloth,
16½", 1950's $12.00-15.00
Buddy Lee, boy with Phillips 66
uniform $95.00-100.00
Mr. Clean, "Mr. Clean", vinyl, 8",
1961 . . . . $25.00-30.00
Uneeda Biscuits, "Uneeda Kid",
Ideal, 16", 1914 . . . $175.00-200.00
Nestles, "Little Hans", vinyl, 12½",
1960's $25.00-30.00
Phillip Morris, "Johnny", composition and cloth, 15" . $80.00-100.00
Cap'n Crunch, cloth, 15½",
1970's $7.00-10.00
RCA 'Sellin' Fool", wood and composition, 15½",
1926 . . . . $175.00-225.00
Seven-up, "Fresh Up Freddie", rubber head, 24",
1958 . . . . $25.00-35.00

Dolls, Antique

Antique dolls, produced from 1850 to
the mid 1930's, have reached a new
high in popularity. Some examples
bring hundreds, even thousands of
dollars. Dolls produced by Armand
Marseille, Schoenhut, Kestner, Simon
& Halbig and other major manufac-

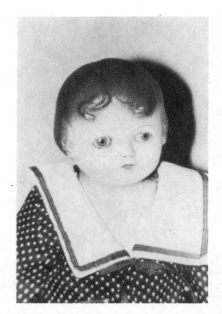

An Ideal Elsie doll from 1919 is valued at $75.00.

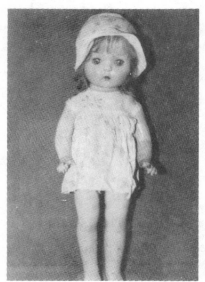

Horsman made this 19½ "Petite Sally composition doll. Today she is worth about
$85.00.

turers usually bring premium prices.
Prices here are for dolls in excellent

A 21½″composition shoulder head girl made by the Metropolitan Doll Company. $75.00.

A 14″doll with poreous bisque head, $225.00.

14″ Composition, Amberg &
    Sons $90.00-100.00
19″ Uncle Sam, Electra Inc.
    N.Y. $350.00-400.00
15″ Scout, Madame
    Hendern $90.00-100.00
15½″ girl, composition head, wood
    body, Horsman . . . $475.00-500.00
19½″ Petite Sally,
    Horsman $80.00-100.00
13½″ Miss Sunshine, Raleigh,
    1918 . . . . $250.00-275.00
26″ singing wax, Webber, musical,
    1880's . . . . $800.00+
14″ composition, American Glueless
    Doll, 1920's $40.00-50.00
23″ socket head, Welsch,
    1916 . . . . $160.00-175.00
23″ Lyf-like, composition,
    1920 . . . . $80.00-100.00

A wax over mache doll from the 1880's $165.00.

condition and completely restored. Beware of new dolls that are made to resemble antique dolls.

Dolls, Armand Marseille

These dolls were manufactured in Germany in the late 1800's and early

This Armand Marseille doll is 21″ tall and has a bisque head on pasteboard and wood body. It is valued at about $200.00.

1900's by the family of Armand Marseille. The dolls have painted porcelain heads and at one time were being produced in greater numbers than any of the other dolls from Europe. Most dolls are marked with an "A.M.". Some are marked "Made in Germany" or "Germany". Don't confuse these with dolls produced in the late 1800's and early 1900's by M.J. Moehling that were also marked with an "AM".

Alma, shoulder plate,
  20″ $200.00
Floradora, shoulder head,
  22″ $200.00
Floradora, sleep eyes,
  19½″ $195.00
Queen Louise, socket head, 24″,
  1910 .... $300.00

My Dream Baby, socket head,
  16″ $450.00
Miss Myrtle, shoulder plate,
  19½″ $225.00
Wonderful Alice, socket head,
  26″ $285.00
My Dearie, socket head, 24″,
  1908-1922 .... $275.00
My Dream Baby, socket head,
  14″ $300.00
Baby Betty, shoulder plate,
  17″ $250.00
Alma, shoulder plate,
  16″ $165.00
Duchess, socket head,
  24″ $310.00
Mabel, shoulder plate,
  18″ $200.00
Bright Eyes, shoulder plate, 21″,
  1890's $225.00
Patrice, socket head,

A 23″ socket head Armand Marseille doll worth about $275.00.

18″ $225.00
Toddler, sleep eyes,
   19″ $400.00
Just Me, bisque head,
   8″ $600.00
Barry, bisque head,
   15″ $1,000.00
Barry, girl version, wax-papier mache
   head, 20″ $450.00

Googlie, snow baby,
   10″ $795.00

Dolls, Barbie

In the past 22 years nearly 100 million Barbie dolls have been sold. Most Barbie dolls on the market today can be bought for around $5.00. But many of the accessories however, bring much

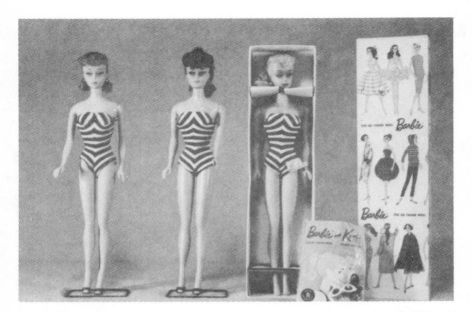

Barbie dolls from 1961, the first hollow body style. Each is worth about $60.00 mint in the original box.

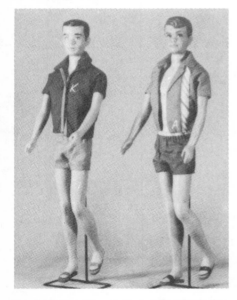

Bendable leg Ken doll and Bendable leg Allen doll from 1964. This type doll is difficult to find and worth about $100.00 mint in the original box.

higher prices. There are many collec-

tors of Barbie dolls and related materials today and the values of the more rare items are increasing.

1959 #1 Barbie doll, mint in
original box . . . . $700.00 +
1959 #2 Barbie doll, mint in
original box . . . . $400.00 +
1963 Fashion Queen Barbie doll,
mint in original
box $65.00-70.00
1965 Bendable Leg Barbie doll,
mint in original
box $40.00-50.00
1967 Black Francie doll, mint in
original box $150.00-160.00
1967 Casey doll, mint in original
box $50.00-60.00
1970 Walking Jamie doll, mint in
original box $50.00-60.00
1971 Malibu Barbie doll, mint in
original box $20.00-25.00
1964 Bendable Leg Ken doll,
mint in original

Barbie Doll cases from the 1960's. $6.00-10.00.

Barbie Kitchen and Barbie Bedroom. $30.00 each, mint.

box $75.00-100.00
1972 Walk Lively Ken doll, mint in
  original box $50.00-60.00
Barbie Photo Album . . $10.00-15.00
Barbie Sportscar, mint in
  original box $45.00-50.00
Barbie Hotrod, mint in
  original box $50.00-60.00
Barbie's Pool Party Set,
  mint in original box . $10.00-15.00
Barbie's Dream House,
  complete $20.00-25.00
Barbie booklet, 1958. . . $10.00-15.00
Barbie & Ken
  Little Theater $65.00-75.00
Barbie's Ten Speeder, mint in
  original box $10.00-15.00
1971 Malibu Ken doll, mint in
  original box $10.00-15.00
1972 Busy Ken doll, mint in
  original box $40.00-45.00

This Effanbee doll is a 24″Honey Ann.
She is a hard plastic walker made in the early 1950's and is worth about $100.00.

Dolls, Effanbee
Dolls produced by the Effanbee Company from the early 1900's until today

An Effanbee Mickey the Clown from 1956.
$15.00.

Effanbee produced this 10½″Lil' Susan
hard plastic doll in the mid 1950's. It is
worth about $12.00 today and if the
original trunk and wardrobe are included
its worth about $32.00.

Effanbee's Baby Bright Eyes from the 1940's has a cloth body and composition head. It is worth about $65.00.

are popular with collectors. The high quality of the materials used as well as the attractiveness of the dolls themselves make them delightful to doll lovers. These dolls are increasing in value and the recent character portrait dolls are very popular.

Patsy, composition,
    14″ $125.00-150.00
Patricia, composition, 15″,
    1932 . . . . $140.00-150.00
Baby Bright Eyes, 14″,
    1940 . . . . $60.00-70.00

Honey Ann, 24″,
    1950's $100.00-115.00
Mickey the Clown, 10″,
    1950's $15.00-20.00
Mary Jane, 30″,
    1960 . . . . $100.00-115.00
Baby Thumkin, 24″,
    1965 . . . . $40.00-50.00
Butterball, 12″,
    1960's $15.00-20.00
Susie Sunshine, 18″,
    1972 . . . . $40.00-50.00
Patsy Ruth, 27″,
    1931 . . . . $150.00-175.00
Button Nose, 8″,
    1940's $40.00-55.00
My Fair Baby, 18″,
    1950's $10.00-15.00
Gumdrop, 16″,
    1960's $15.00-25.00
Pumpkin, 11″,
    1920's $5.00-10.00
Ann Shirley, 15″,
    1954 . . . . $60.00-70.00

Dolls, French

Antique dolls produced in France have become very popular and valuable in this country. The original beauty and craftsmanship are still evident in these dolls and, for well-represented examples in original dress, prices soar. Bru dolls seem to be especially desirable.

Ferte′, closed mouth, 12″,
    1870's . . . . $1,000.00 +
Fleischmann & Blodel, Eden Be′be′,
    20½″ $700.00-900.00
Jumeau, open mouth, jointed composition body,
    17″ $500.00-700.00
Jumeau, jointed, closed mouth, pierced ears,
    19½″ $500.00-700.00

These dolls are French made Jumeaus from the early 1900's. Each is worth $450.00-$700.00.

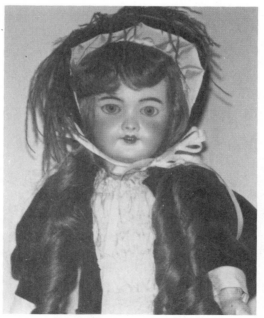

A 26″SFBJ French doll with sleep eyes and open mouth, $500.00-$700.00.

Raberry & Delphieu, jointed
  composition body,
  15 " . . . . $1,000.00 +
Schmitt & Fils, jointed body,
  15 " . . . . $2,000.00 +
S.F.B.J., boy, jointed body,
  14 " . . . . $1,000.00 +
S.F.B.J., 5-piece body,
  10 " $150.00-200.00
Jules Steiner, pierced ears, mache
  body, 11 " . . . . $1,000.00 +
Unis, 5-piece body,
  12 " $150.00-250.00

Dolls, German

German dolls are especially appealing
to doll collectors. Best known for the
children and lifelike babies, these dolls
are relatively expensive when in
original clothes and in good condition.
Also see Armand Marseille, Kestner
and Simon & Halbig.

Arranbee, baby, 10½ " head
  circumference $200.00-250.00
C.M. Bergmann, bisque socket head,
  12 " $200.00-250.00

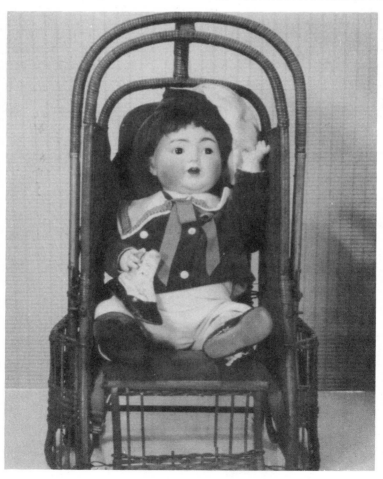

This 24 "Kammer & Rinehardt doll is valued at $500.00-600.00.

112

A German Kammer and Rinehardt doll with bisque head on composition body, $500.00-$600.00. The stuffed animals are Steiff and worth $50.00-$100.00 for the small one and $200.00 for the large one.

C & D Dressel, lady, composition jointed body,
14½ " $500.00-600.00
Heubach & Kopplesdorf, black mother (9½ ") and
baby (5 ") $500.00-600.00
Kley & Hahn, bisque head boy, composition body, 18 "$1,000.00+
Revalo, bisque head, composition body, 21 " $300.00-350.00
Bruno Schmidt, girl, sleep eyes, protruding tongue,
14 " $250.00-300.00
Bruno Schmidt, Tommy Tucker, composition body,
22 " .... $1,000.00+
Herm Steiner, new born baby,
14 " $250.00-300.00
Louis Wolf, baby, 15 " head, circumference $300.00-350.00

Dolls, Kestner

J.D. Kestner was a manufacturer of German dolls in the 19th and early 20th centuries. The company produc-

ed many kinds of dolls and most are marked with a crown. Kestner was one of the earlier producers of dolls with sleep eyes. As in the case of all German dolls, Kestner dolls are quite valuable.

17 " shoulder head, kid body, bisque arms, open mouth $350.00
13 " socket head, composition jointed body, open
mouth $250.00
15 " shoulder head, kid body, bisque arms, closed mouth $450.00
18½ " turned shoulder head, kidoline body, bisque arms, open/closed mouth $250.00
15 " shoulder head, kid body, bisque arms, open/closed mouth . $250.00
18½ " shoulder head, kid body, sleeps eyes, molded teeth . $185.00
20½ " socket head on bisque shoulder plate, closed
mouth $550.00
15 " socket head on 5 piece baby

This Kestner 18″ socket head doll with bent leg body is worth about $300.00.

body, bent leg, open
mouth $250.00
14″ socket head on 5 piece baby
body, bent leg, brush stroke
hair $165.00
16″ socket head, composition body,
pierced ears, open mouth . $150.00

Dolls, Madame Alexander
Madame Alexander dolls are probably

the most collected dolls in the world. Hundreds of different dolls have been designed by Madame Alexander in the past 52 years, giving the collector a very wide range from which to choose. Prices here are for dolls in mint or near mint condition. Dolls in original boxes would be valued slightly higher.

Active Miss, 18″, 1954 . . . . . $135.00

A 7½" set of Dionne Quints dolls with their own ferris wheel. These 1936 dolls are valued at about $100.00 each.

A Madame Alexander 14" Easter Doll from 1968. Only 300 of these outfits were produced so this doll is valued at $900.00 and up.

Binnie Walker, skater, 15",
  1955 .... $165.00
Curly Locks, 7½", 1955 .... $250.00
Debutant, 18", 1953 .... $325.00
Drum Majorette, 7½",
  1955 .... $300.00
English Guard, 8", 1900's .. $400.00
Finnish, 7", 1930's $150.00
Girl on trapeze, 40", 1951 .. $375.00
Hedy LaMarr, 17", 1940's .. $325.00
Ice Skater, 8", 1950's $145.00
June Bride, 21" $450.00
Klondike Kate, 11",
  1960's .... $850.00 +
Lady Churchill, 18", 1950's . $325.00
Dolly Madison, 1976 .... $165.00

A Madame Alexander 15" Annabelle is hard plastic and worth about $165.00.

115

Nancy Drew, 12″, 1960's . . . $300.00
Orchard Princess, 21″ $450.00
Prince Charles, 8″, 1950's . . $275.00
Ringbearer, 14″, 1950's $275.00
Smokey Tail, 1930's $300.00
Tea Party, 8″, 1950's $145.00
Tweedle-Dum & Tweedle-Dee,
   14″ $300.00
Virginia Dare, 9″, 1940's . . . $175.00
Wendy Angel, 8″, 1950's . . . $600.00
Yolanda, 12″, 1960's $135.00
Zorina Ballerina, 17″,
   1930's $275.00

Dolls, Modern

Modern dolls, those produced from the 1930's to present, are extremely popular flea market items. These modern dolls have contributed greatly to the overall appeal of the doll collecting hobby. Dolls not currently in production or discontinued variations of current dolls are most collectible. Character dolls, especially those of the

Arranbee made this Nancy doll. She is composition and stands 17″tall, $75.00.

This 14″Toni doll was made by Ideal in the late 1940's. Today it is valued at about $55.00.

An 18″Ideal Miss Revelon doll from the 1950's worth about $45.00.

1930's and 1940's are much in demand.

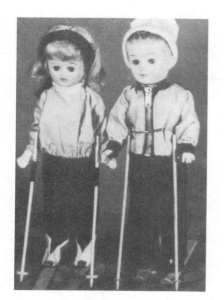

Vogue's Jill and Jeff dolls in their original ski outfits. They are worth $30.00-$35.00.

Gigi, A & H Doll Co., 7½",
1950's $3.00-5.00
Bride, American Character, 18",
1950's $40.00-50.00
Barbara Streisand, Japan,
14" $80.00-100.00
Honey West, Gilbert, 11½",
1965's $20.00-25.00
Mary Poppins, vinyl,
1960's $20.00-25.00
Betsy Wetsy, Ideal,
12" $15.00-20.00
John F. Kennedy, vinyl head,
13" $30.00-40.00
Hiker, Lenci, 9" $100.00-125.00
Dr. Doolittle, Mattel, 6",
1960's $12.00-15.00
Joe Namath, Mego,
12" $20.00-25.00
Baby First Born, Uneeda, 13",
1960's $2.00-3.00
Lois Jane, composition, Vanity, 19",
1940 . . . . $20.00-25.00
Nancy, Arranbee, 17" . $75.00-85.00

Daniel Boone, plastic face, plush
body, 20", 1950's . . . $25.00-30.00
Cindy Strutter, Horsman, hard
plastic, 1950's $80.00-90.00
Lucy Mae, Dakin, cloth, 24",
1960's $15.00-20.00
Patti Playpal, Ideal,
1961 . . . . $75.00-90.00
Terri Lee,
Brownie uniform . . $80.00-100.00

Dolls, Oriental

Many unusual and interesting dolls
have been produced in China, Japan,
Korea, Thailand, and other Oriental
countries. These dolls range from simple folk figures to very detailed pieces
of art and the price range corresponds.

Chinese Old Lady, straw stuffed
cloth, 10½" $50.00-60.00
China, fisherman, composition,
12" $50.00-60.00
Japan, clay & composition, glass eyes,
32" . . . . $500.00+

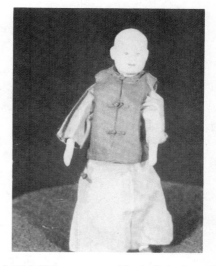

A 10" Chinese man with cloth body and composition head, hands, and feet. $42.50.

117

This 12" Chinese Weaving Girl has a wire armature body and composition head. It is worth about $60.00-$65.00.

Japan, Aki Hito, composition body, 14" $275.00-325.00

Japan, Sakura, straw & cloth, 8" $60.00-65.00

Japan, Yamoto Ning Yo children, composition bodies, 13½" $15.00-20.00

Japan, Hakata figures, painted mache $10.00-15.00

Thailand, dancer, painted cloth, 7" $8.00-10.00

Korea, lady, cloth, silk face, 8" $8.00-10.00

India, bride & groom, cloth, 12" $15.00-20.00

Dolls, Simon & Halbig

Simon & Halbig manufactured dolls

An 18″ Simon and Halbig socket head doll with mechanical key wind movement, $550.00.

from the latter part of the 19th century until the 1930's. It became one of the largest German firms and made heads for many French doll makers in the 1870's and 1880's. Many of the Simon & Halbig dolls had moveable eyes. Like other German dolls of the period, these high quality dolls have high price tags.

Socket head, jointed composition body, sleep eyes, 21″.....$185.00
Socket head, composition body, closed mouth, pierced ears, 18″ $650.00
Socket head, composition body, set eyes, closed mouth, 25″ $695.00
Shoulder head, cloth body, bisque

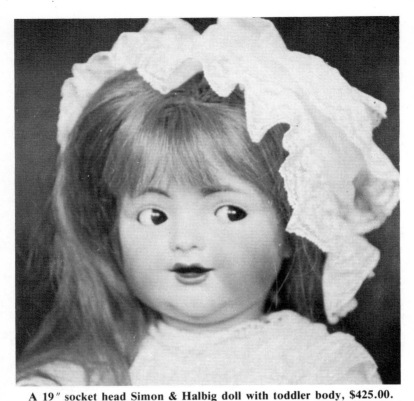

A 19″ socket head Simon & Halbig doll with toddler body, $425.00.

arms, sleep eyes, 8″ $250.00

Shoulder head, kid body, bisque arms,
  pierced ears, 19½″ $250.00

Brown bisque socket head,
  composition body, sleep eyes
  16″ $500.00

Shoulder head, kid/muslin body,
  bisque arms, open mouth,
  29″ $450.00

Shoulder head, kid body, bisque
  forearms, open mouth,
  24″ $265.00

Socket head, key wind mechanical
  walker, flirty eyes, pierced ears,
  18″ $550.00

Socket head, 5 piece body,
  sleep eyes, 22″ $325.00

Dolls, Trolls

Trolls were first popular with kids in
the early 1960's as good luck charms
and novelty dolls. Most are worth only a few dollars but some can be
valuable and the non-doll trolls are interesting art pieces.

Wish Nik, bride & groom, Uneeda,
  5½″ $6.00-10.00

Wish Nik, vinyl, mohair,
  plastic eyes, 3″ $3.00-6.00

Viking, wood,
  made in Denmark $3.00-5.00

Wish Nik, hula girl,
  5½″ $15.00-23.00

Batman, unmarked, 3″ . . $6.00-12.00

Design Dam horse, 3″ . $10.00-15.00

Neanderthal Man, Bijou Toy,
  1963 . . . . $12.00-18.00

Graduate, unmarked,
  5½″ $5.00-8.00

3" Wish Nik trolls worth about $3.00-$6.00 each.

A 12" two-headed troll. $75.00-$90.00.

Hobbit, Royalty Design,
   1970's $5.00-7.00
Two-headed Wish Nik .$12.00-20.00

Elvis Collectibles

Elvis Presley was probably the most promoted singer to ever appear in this country. Literally hundreds of different items were sold with his likeness

An early 1956 Elvis Presley souvenir picture album worth about $200.00-$250.00.

and tied-in with movies, records, and concerts. Early Elvis items are most popular (1956 to early 1960's) but some later items are also quite valuable.

Doll, with original clothing, 18",
   1957................$1,000.00+
Dog-tag sweater holder, on card,
   1950's $90.00-100.00
Record case, 7½"x7½",
   1956.............$150.00-175.00
Ashtray with photo, 3½",
   1950's $65.00-90.00
Plastic statue, Elvis & guitar,
   7½", 1950's $350.00-450.00
Canvas sneakers $200.00-225.00
Pencil pack of 12 pencils, unopened,
   1950's $60.00-85.00
Glass mug, *GI Blues*...$40.00-65.00
Record catalog, 1968 ..$15.00-18.00
Postcard, Elvis's gold car,
   1960's $10.00-15.00

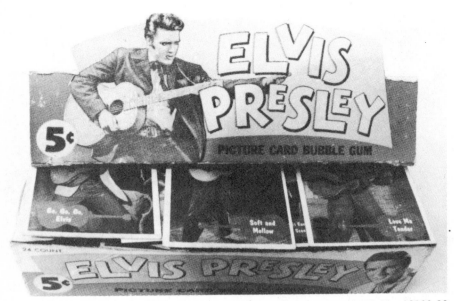

1956 bubblegum card box. This box is a rare item and brings about $150.00 to $200.00 today.

Elvis Presley Enterprises pencils in the original cellophane packages. $60.00-$85.00.

Pressbook from *That's the Way It Is*. $15.00.

Window card from *Wild in the Country*, 1961. $25.00.

Sheet music,
"Ask Me" $12.00-15.00
Sheet music,
"Almost" $10.00-12.00
Tour photo album,
1956 ....$60.00-80.00
Menu, International Hotel,
1970 ....$25.00-30.00
Magazine, *Elvis In The Army*,
1959 ....$35.00-40.00
Magazine, *T.V. Guide*,
May 7, 1960 ....$30.00-40.00
Movie poster, *Love Me Tender*,
27"x41" $125.00-150.00
Tabloid herald, *King Creole*,
1958 ....$15.00-18.00
Book, *Operation Elvis*, with dust
jacket, 1960 ....$50.00-60.00
Coloring contest sheet,
Blue Hawaii $15.00-20.00

Farm Antiques

If it was used on the farm, it's now collectible. Farm tools head the list that also includes dairy equipment, poultry producing aids, household items, etc. (Also check Primitives and Tool sections.)

Hay hook, wrought iron,
9" $7.00-10.00
Feed grinder, hand crank,
16" tall $15.00-25.00
Barn pulley, hardwood wheel,
cast iron frame $10.00-15.00
Implement seat, cast iron,
unmarked $10.00-15.00
Grain scoop, metal with wood
handle $15.00-20.00
Egg crate, wood slat...$30.00-40.00
Egg shipping container, metal,
hinged top $20.00-25.00
Herb dryer, wood slats,
approximately 2'x3'.$40.00-50.00
Dipper, tin, one quart .$10.00-15.00
Corn husking hook, leather palm
guard, laces $8.00-10.00
Row guide stakes, iron, 26",
pair $5.00-8.00
Meat hook, iron and wood,

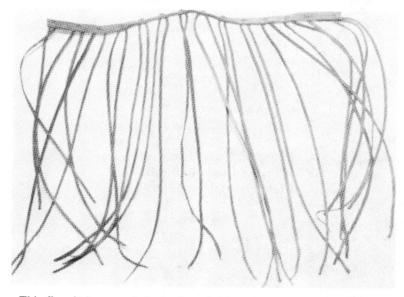

This flyswitch covered the back and sides of a horse and mule. $3.50.

A tobacco hiller used in the 1800's on a Kentucky farm. $35.00-$45.00.

An early harrow. $25.00.

8″ $8.00-10.00

Bee smoker,
tin with bellows $20.00-25.00

Potato grading table, hardwood, four
hole sizes $60.00-80.00

Milk can, tin with lid,
handle $18.00-25.00

Wagon seat, iron spring & arms,
wood seat & back ... $50.00-75.00

Egg scale, arm & weight,
metal egg cup $5.00-10.00

Corn husking pegs, hardwood,
leather finger thongs ... $3.00-5.00

Chick fountain,
stoneware $20.00-30.00

Bull ring, copper, 3″
diameter $5.00-10.00

Fiesta

Fiesta is a brightly colored, heavy ironstone dinnerware produced by the Homer Laughlin Co. from 1936 until 1971. The lines and styles of this popular collectible are right out of the

A Fiesta juice pitcher and 5 oz. tumblers.

Covered Fiesta refrigerator jars and covered jugs. The refrigerator jars are worth $45.00-$55.00 and the jugs, $65.00-$75.00.

A Fiesta footed salad bowl. This item was discontinued in the 1940's and today is worth $62.00-$68.00.

A Fiesta fruit bowl made only in the late 1930's and early 1940's. $47.00-$55.00.

Art Deco period. Fiesta pieces are easily recognized because of their bright, gay colors, smooth graceful lines and distinctive pattern shapes. Originally Fiesta was produced in red, dark blue, old ivory, yellow, light green, and turquois. Though there were other colors produced, anything but these are of later manufacture. Harlequin & Riviera, similar but less expensive lines of dinnerware, were also produced by Homer Laughlin Co.

Carafe, 3 pint $35.00-45.00

Marmalade $47.00-55.00
Candleholders, bulb
   type $20.00-25.00
French casserole,
   yellow $65.00-75.00
Ice pitcher, 6-8 oz. tumblers,
   metal holder $60.00-80.00
Divided plate $7.00-10.00
Dessert bowl, 6" $6.00-9.00
Platter, oval, 12"...... $9.00-13.00
Sauceboat $8.50-13.00
Covered casserole $25.00-30.00
Relish tray $38.00-45.00
Covered onion soup ... $65.00-80.00
Vase, 8" $75.00-85.00
Candleholders, tripod .. $65.00-75.00
Juice pitcher, yellow,
   30 oz $7.00-10.00
Juice pitcher, red or gray,
   30 oz. $30.00-40.00
Juice tumbler, 5 oz. ... $10.00-20.00
Individual sugar, creamer and
   tray $45.00-50.00
Ashtray $12.00-15.00
Sweets comport $12.00-16.00
Syrup pitcher $55.00-70.00
After dinner coffee
   cups $12.00-15.00
Cream soup cup $10.00-15.00
Tom & Jerry mug $15.00-20.00
Tom & Jerry mug, red . $30.00-40.00

Fire Fighting Collectibles

Anything related to fighting and detecting fires is considered collectible. Personal items used by firemen, station house equipment, fire fighting equipment, home extinguishers, parade uniforms, etc., all are subjects of search by enthusiasts of fire fighting. Early items, such as leather helmets and buckets are especially desirable. Also equipment made from brass, copper, gold and silver demands a higher price.

Extinguisher, brass, "Safeguard",
18″ $25.00-30.00
Helmet, leather, greyhound
holder .... $250.00+
Firehouse gong, oak
case .... $1,500.00+
Engine lights from Hook & Ladder,
colored glass .... $2,000.00+
Parade belt $25.00-35.00
Helmet, plastic $10.00-15.00
Postcard, firemen with ladder
truck, pre 1920's $5.00-10.00
Postcard, firemen with horse-
drawn pumper,
1900's $5.00-10.00
Leather bucket, decorated,
1800's $225.00-300.00
Fire alarm box, cast iron, Chicago,

An early leather fire bucket marked "N.M.
No. 14". $250.00 and up.

1920's $250.00-275.00
Speaking trumpet, silver-
plate .... $400.00+
Hose nozzle, brass,
12″ $20.00-25.00
Extinguisher, brass, "Fyr-Fyter",
18″ $20.00-25.00
Fire mark, tree, cast
iron $100.00-125.00
Uniform shirt, flap front, red
wool $60.00-70.00

Flow Blue

Flow Blue is an English china. During
the firing, the blue appears to have run
from the design giving the china a
smeared look. Pieces of Flow Blue
were made in many patterns in the
1800's by several different potteries.
Collectors are paying high prices for
good quality Flow Blue today. The
following listings include pattern
names.

"Yeddo", soup bowl,
10″ $40.00-45.00
"Cambridge", platter,
11″x16″ $130.00-140.00
"Rose", cream &
sugar $75.00-100.00
"Manhattan", plate ... $20.00-25.00
"Eclipse", gravy boat . $60.00-65.00
"Bristol", vegetable
bowl $100.00-125.00
"Jewel", plate, small .. $20.00-25.00
"Verona", platter $60.00-80.00
"Temple", plate, 10″ .. $50.00-55.00
"La Belle", covered syrup
pitcher $40.00-50.00
"Italia", cup and
saucer $60.00-65.00
"Crumlin", 40 piece
set .... $1,000.00+
"Monarch", 24 piece
set .... $700.00+

A flow blue saucer showing how the color seems to "bleed" out of the lines.

"Kyber", octagon plate,
4" $75.00-100.00
"Linda", platter $50.00-60.00
"Oriental", bone
dish $45.00-50.00
"La Belle", vegetable
bowl $50.00-60.00
"Hong Kong",
teapot $150.00-175.00
"Celtic", bone dish . . . $20.00-30.00
"Argyle", platter $60.00-75.00

Fountain Pens

Only recently have collectors been grabbing up all of those beautiful old fountain pens that were so commonplace in the 1920's, 30's and 40's. The most popular are the name brands and the most valuable are the gold pens. Many sets of fountain pens with matching pencils can be found and since this hobby is still relatively new, prices are fairly reasonable for quality items. Prices here are for pens in excellent condition and in working order. The alert collector should also be on the lookout for damaged or worn pens to be used as parts in repairing similar pens.

Waterman
Patrician, 1928 . . . . $70.00-75.00
Commando, 1943 . . . . . $10.00-15.00
Citation, 1946 . . . . $8.00-10.00
Ideal Ink View, 1942 . . $12.00-15.00
Lady Patricia, 1928 . . . . $15.00-20.00
54 Ripple, 1923 . . . . $25.00-30.00

Parker
Lady Duofold, 1923 . . . $25.00-30.00
Vacumatic, 1932 . . . . . . $20.00-25.00
51 Pencil, 1942 . . . . $30.00-35.00
51 Pen, 1942 . . . . $60.00-65.00

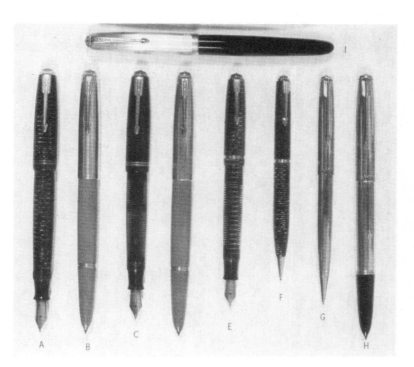

Parker pens from the 1940's.

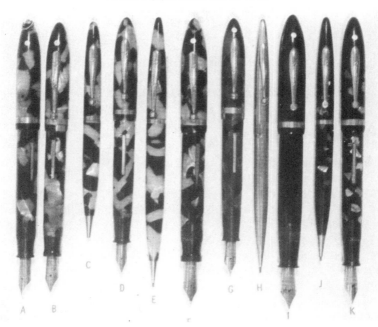

Sheaffer pens from 1930 to 1936.

Sheaffer pens from 1913 to 1930.

Vacumatic, 1946 . . . . $7.00-10.00

Sheaffer

White Dot Lifetime,
  1928 . . . . $80.00-85.00
White Dot Lifetime pencil,
  1928 . . . . $50.00-60.00
Ladies White Dot Lifetime,
  1926 . . . . $10.00-12.00
Valiant White Dot,
  1941 . . . . $7.00-10.00
Triumph Lifetime pen,
  1942 . . . . $30.00-35.00
Triumph pencil,
  1942 . . . . $7.00-10.00
400 Fineline pencil,
  1946 . . . . $5.00-10.00

875 Tuckaway, 1947 . . . . $7.00-10.00
Statesman, 1949 . . . . $10.00-12.00

Wahl-Eversharp

Midget, 1933 . . . . $12.00-15.00
Skyline, 1941 . . . . $5.00-7.00
$64 pen, 1944 . . . . $40.00-50.00
Fifth Avenue, 1944 . . . . $15.00-20.00
Fifth Avenue pencil,
  1944 . . . . $7.00-10.00

Franciscan Ware

Franciscan pottery was produced in
California. The company is generally
known for its dinnerware and some art
pieces. The pieces are generally

Franciscan Padua table ware. Toast cover, $20.00-$25.00; cream jug, $12.00; sugar with lid, $10.00; tab handled cereal, $6.00; plate, $7.00; egg cup, $6.00; 6½″ plate, $4.00; cup, $6.00; saucer, $2.00; salt and pepper, $10.00; tumbler, $7.00; coffee jug and stopper, $15.00; 12″ plate, $15.00.

Franciscan Coronado Art Ware vase from the late 1930's or early 1940's. $14.00-$18.00.

simplistic in style with geometric shapes being very popular.

El Patio, oval serving
    bowl $6.00-8.00
El Patio, Toby mug,
    7½″ $10.00-20.00
Coronado tea set, creamer, sugar,
    teapot, white $40.00-60.00
Montecito, egg cup, coral
    satin $3.00-5.00
Montecito, teapot, light
    blue $10.00-12.00
Padua, cream jug $12.00-14.00
Padua, hors d'oeuvre
    tray $35.00-45.00
Tropico, pitcher, 5¾″ . . . $7.00-9.00
Ruby, after dinner pot . $35.00-40.00
Capistrano, leaf shaped
    bowl $5.00-12.00
Catalina, ribbed vase . . $14.00-16.00
Ox Blood, vase, 11″ . . . $45.00-65.00

Nautical, cornucopia shell
vase $9.00-14.00
Hotel plate, sectional,
10½ " $9.00-12.00
Cocinero, ramekin,
green $7.00-9.00

Fruit Jars

Fruit jars are glass jars that can be sealed from the outside air and are used in preserving fruits and vegetables. Through the years, the jars have had very few changes. The enclosures, on the other hand, have had a gradual evolution from clamps, bails, glass lids and other complicated devices to today's easy-to-use models. Fruit jars are available in many sizes and colors and have been manufactured by a multitude of companies. Prices here are for jars with the original enclosures, and no cracks or chips. Factory flaws are sometimes desirable if the flaw is a rare type.

Acme Seal, glass top, zinc
band $20.00-25.00
Almy, aqua, quart, glass
lid $75.00-85.00
B&B, amber, quart, glass
lid $2.00-3.00
Bennett's No. 1, clear, zinc
lid $150.00-200.00
Best, aqua, quart, glass
lid $20.00-25.00
Blue Ribbon, clear, quart, glass
lid $6.00-8.00
Chatanooga Mason, clear, zinc
lid $4.00-6.00
Cassidy, aqua, quart, glass lid,
wire bail $150.00-175.00
Conserve Jar, clear, quart,
glass lid $6.00-8.00
Dexter, aqua, quart, glass
lid $25.00-30.00

Dominion, clear, glass
lid $75.00-100.00
Eagle, green, quart,
wax seal $70.00-75.00
Excelsior, aqua, quart,
glass lid $90.00-100.00
The Gem, aqua, quart,
wax seal $8.00-10.00
Hamilton, blue, quart,
glass lid $40.00-50.00
The Hero, aqua, quart,
glass lid $30.00-35.00
The Ideal, aqua,
zinc lid $15.00-18.00
K-G, clear, pint,
zinc lid $1.00-3.00
King, clear, glass lid,
wire bail $12.00-15.00
KYGW, aqua, quart,
wax seal $18.00-20.00
L&W, amber, quart,
wax seal $25.00-30.00
Lightning, aqua, glass lid,
wire bail $4.00-6.00
The Nifty, clear, quart,

Mason's patent 1858 fruit jar. Beware of the dates on some fruit jars: they do not necessarily date the jar.

glass lid $25.00-30.00
Pansy, aqua, quart . . $125.00-150.00
Princess, aqua, glass lid,
   wire bail $12.00-15.00
Protector, aqua, quart,
   metal lid $35.00-40.00
Reid, aqua, quart . . . $250.00-300.00
Root, aqua, pint,
   zinc lid $5.00-7.00
Safe, clear, tin disc,
   spring clip $8.00-10.00
Sanford 327, aqua, quart,
   zinc lid $5.00-7.00
Societe, clear, glass lid,
   wire bail $2.00-4.00
Star, aqua, quart,
   glass lid $70.00-75.00
Sure, aqua, glass lid,
   spring clip $200.00-225.00
Tillyer, aqua, quart,
   glass lid $75.00-100.00
Union 5, aqua, quart,
   wax seal $35.00-40.00
Vacuum, clear, pint . . . $10.00-15.00
Victory 1925, clear,
   glass lid $4.00-6.00
W, aqua, wax seal $3.00-5.00
Woodbury, aqua, 3 sizes,
   glass lid $20.00-25.00
Worcester, aqua, quart,
   tapered stopper $85.00-100.00

A slat-back chair from the early 1800's. $160.00-$200.00.

Furniture, Country

Country furniture is generally primitive in nature with many items being handmade. Most are of good solid construction and simplicity is evident. Be especially aware of pieces with hand-planed surfaces, dovetailed edges and original paint finishes. Be careful to avoid recent reproductions since this furniture has become popular with decorators.

Dough chest, pine, 4 legs,

This step-back cupboard is from the 1850's and valued at $900.00-$1,100.00.

The small kitchen storage cupboard is worth about $450.00-$600.00. The chairs are worth about $125.00 and up.

1850's $175.00-200.00
Tavern table, tilt top, round,
    1800's . . . . $700.00+
Sheraton stand table, cherry,
    one drawer $150.00-200.00
Blanket chest, 32"x27"x21", dovetailing, walnut . . . . $300.00+
Sugar chest, maple, bottom drawer,
    1850's . . . . $600.00+
Cupboard, glass top doors,
    wood bottom doors,
    walnut . . . . $875.00+
Step-back cupboard,
    3 doors . . . . $800.00+
Apple sorters chair,
    splint seat $300.00-400.00
Child's chair, slat back, arms,
    1850's $375.00-450.00
Arrow back chair, plank
    bottom, 1850's $150.00-200.00
Storage cupboard, Ohio, 2 doors,
    1800's $450.00-550.00
Dry sink, extended trough,
    pine, 1850's $800.00-1,000.00
Chimney cupboard, pine, original
    paint $550.00-600.00

"Mammy" bench, rocking settee,
    place for infants . . . . . . $800.00+
Corner cupboard, 4 door,
    walnut . . . . $3,000.00+
Jelly cabinet, 1 drawer, 2 doors,
    walnut . . . . $500.00+

Furniture, Oak

Oak furniture has become one of the most popular types of antique furniture available today. Its sturdy construction combined with the solidness of the wood give it the ability to stand up for years. There are two main types of Oak, regular sawed and quarter sawed. The quarter sawed wood gives the furniture's grain a "radiating" look. Prices here are for furniture that is excellent quality, refinished and restored.

Folding bed . . . . $400.00+
Book case, 1 door,
    glass $225.00-250.00
Book case, 2 doors, glass . $500.00+
Book case, sectional . . . . . $400.00+

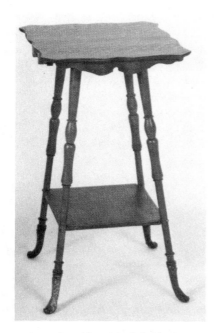

**An oak table with dolphin feet.
$100.00-$115.00.**

Buffet . . . . $500.00 +
Chairs, dining, cane seats, set of
    four . . . . $475.00 +
Chairs, dining, leather bottom, set
    of four . . . . $425.00 +
Chairs, dining, wood seats, set of
    four . . . . $400.00 +
Chairs, kitchen, cane seats, set of
    four . . . . $300.00 +
Chairs, kitchen, leather seats, set
    of four . . . . $300.00 +
Chairs, kitchen, wood seats, set
    of four . . . . $200.00 +
Desk chair, swivel . . . $150.00-250.00
Desk chair, straight . . . $75.00-125.00
Rocking chair,
    carved $175.00-275.00
Rocking chair, plain . . $80.00-100.00
Rocking chair,
    upholstered $180.00-275.00
Rocking chair, cane
    seat $200.00-250.00

**Swivel oak pressback chair.
$300.00-$325.00.**

Children's rocking chair,
    carved $150.00-200.00
Children's rocking chair,
    plain $75.00-125.00
Chiffonier . . . . $200.00 +
Chifforobe $140.00-200.00
China cabinet, glass
    front . . . . $500.000 +
China cabinet, small,
    plain . . . . $375.00 +
Couch . . . . $450.00 +
Davenport . . . . $300.00 +
Desk, small ladies . . . . . . $375.00 +
Desk, drop front . . . . $275.00 +
Desk, small
    missionary $150.00-175.00
Desk, large rolltop . . . . . $1,200.00 +
Desk, small rolltop . . . . . . $300.00 +

A hall stand that would anchor to the wall. $300.00-$350.00.

Desk, stand-up	$450.00 +
Dresser	$200.00 +
Dresser, Princess	$200.00 +
Dresser, small, plain	$150.00 +
Hall rack, with seat	$500.00 +
Hall rack, with seat, small	$425.00 +
Kitchen cabinet	$275.00 +

Kitchen cabinet with leaded
glass . . . . $375.00 +
Kitchen cabinet with frosted
glass . . . . $375.00 +
Stand-up mirror $200.00-225.00
Hanging mirror $65.00-80.00
Kitchen table $100.00-150.00
Round pedestal table . . . . $450.00 +
Round pedestal tabel with claw
feet . . . . $575.00 +
Stand table $100.00-150.00
End table $80.00-125.00
Wash stands $170.00-275.00
Oval mirror $50.00-100.00
Shaving mug rack . . . $220.00-300.00
Barber's cabinet . . . . $350.00 +
Medicine cabinet $50.00-100.00
Music cabinet . . . . $125.00 +
Wardrobe . . . . $325.00 +
Pedestal, ornate $90.00-125.00
Pedestal, plain $60.00-75.00
Stool, swivel with
back $100.00-200.00
Stool, swivel, no
back $80.00-100.00
Stool $65.00-85.00
Card file cabinet,
8 drawer $190.00-225.00
Card file cabinet, with roll
front . . . . $300.00 +
Dish cupboard, glass
doors . . . . $325.00 +
Dish cupboard, no glass . . $200.00 +
Sleigh bed . . . . $250.00 +
Settee . . . . $275.00 +
Ice box, 75 lb. . . . . $250.00 +
Ice box, 100 lb. . . . . $375.00 +
Ice box, chest type . . . . . . $250.00 +
Dining table, square . . . . . $200.00 +
Library table, oval . . . . . . $200.00 +
Round end table $80.00-100.00
Umbrella stand $60.00-75.00
Piano bench $80.00-95.00
Piano stool $80.00-100.00
Mirror with shelf $110.00-125.00

A buffet with leaded glass doors. $600.00-$650.00.

An early 1900's chiffonier, $325.00-$345.00.

Furniture, Victorian

The beautiful hard woods combined with the decorative detailing of the pieces make Victorian furniture very attractive to consumers. The period pieces are usually very distinctive and

A Victorian Renaissance desk worth $2,500.00 and up.

Victorian Rococo Revival sofa. $800.00-$875.00.

ornate with generous use of walnut, mahagany and oak. The workmanship is usually of excellent quality and the prices reflect that quality and beauty.

Bookcase desk, Eastlake, walnut and burl, 1870's . . . . $800.00 +
S-Roll Top desk, cherry, 52″x46″x28″ . . . . $3,200.00 +
Cylinder secretary, walnut and burl, glass doors . . . . $2,500.00 +
Wine cabinet, Empire, mahogany and burl . . . . $800.00 +
Umbrella stand, walnut, turned posts $200.00-225.00
Game table, mahogany, vase post $500.00-600.00
Halfround table, carved swan head & wings $375.00-450.00
Corner whatnot, molded edge, 5 tier . . . . $265.00 +
Davenport desk, side drawers, walnut $750.00-850.00

Wishbone dresser, marble shelf, walnut . . . . $1,300.00 +
Piano stool, maple, ball and claw feet, round $125.00-175.00
Candlestand, carved stags head, walnut $175.00-200.00
Dining table, walnut, turned legs, claw feet, 6 chairs . . . . $1,500.00 +
Wardrobe, mahogany, Rococo style . . . . $1,800.00 +
Washstand, walnut, marble top and splashback $475.00-500.00
Pie cooling rack, maple, tilting shelves $125.00-145.00
Floor screen, tapestry, walnut adjustable frame . . $195.00-225.00
High chair, pull-up, Eastlake, cane seat & back $175.00-200.00
Small table, spool turned legs, 25″ tall $125.00-175.00
Desk chair, walnut, cane seat, swivels . . . . $500.00 +

This Victorian cylinder secretary is walnut and burl and is valued at $2,500.00 and up.

A wicker rocker. $100.00-$115.00.

Wicker rocker. $85.00-$95.00.

Furniture, Wicker

Wicker was first imported into the United States from the Orient in the 18th century. By the middle of the 1800's, it was being manufactured in America. Elaborate styles were popular at first, followed by a plainer design. Naturally, the older pieces are more valuable than the more recently produced wicker. The collector should take caution when buying wicker because many pieces are being manufactured today. A good general rule of thumb in determining the age of wicker is to study the thickness of the weave. Before 1900 the reed was of a light quality and woven very close. After 1900, a heavier reed with a loose weaving pattern came into use.

Straight chair $125.00-200.00
Davenport . . . . $350.00+
Hamper $35.00-40.00
Straight, fireside chair . . . . $200.00+
Lounge . . . . $250.00+
Rocking chair $125.00-200.00
Tea cart . . . . $200.00+

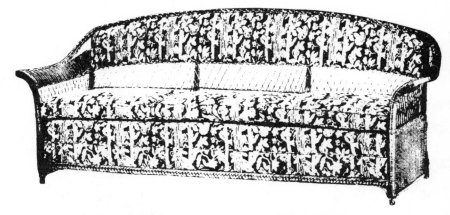

An upholstered wicker davenport. $260.00-$285.00.

A wicker side chair. $130.00-$155.00.

Baby buggy $125.00-200.00
Library table $115.00-175.00
Planter..............$95.00-125.00
Round table $175.00-225.00
Settee $250.00-300.00
Footstool............$30.00-40.00

Gambling Devices

Gambling games of chance, cheating devices, machines and pieces of games are all collectible. Slot machines, once common in many public places prior to the Depression, are in great demand as are "layouts" or surfaces designed for gambling games. Cheating devices, because of their rarity, usually command a large price tag. Prices for gambling machines are for those in excellent working condition.

Slot machine, Jennings Club Chief,
   1940's ....$1,700.00 +
Gambler's dirk, pearl handled, 4 "
   blade $200.00-225.00
Dice cage, 10 " high,
   3 dice.............$85.00-100.00
Dice cups, French, ornate with coat of
   arms...............$25.00-35.00
Poker chips, Jockey Club, horse
   & rider on 100 boxed
   chips $25.00-30.00
Tintype photo, 3 men
   playing cards $50.00-60.00
Roulette wheel, 14½ ",
   wood $260.00-275.00
Faro chip rack, cloth covered,
   24 "x12 " $150.00-175.00
Dice stick and card turner,
   wood set $50.00-60.00
Horse race wheel, 30 ",
   color horses $230.00-250.00
Catalog, Hunt & Company, gambling
   equipment $50.00-75.00

Early "Steamboat" playing cards were commonly used by gamblers. $35.00-$65.00 for full decks.

Leather dice cups. $25.00-$50.00 each.

Slot machine, Buckley Bones,
1930's ....$2,500.00 +
Slot machine, C & F Baby Grand,
1930's ....$1,500.00 +
Slot Machine, Jennings Little Duke,
1930's ....$2,000.00 +
Slot machine, Mills Black Cherry,
1940's ....$1,200.00 +
Slot machine, Mills Jewel,
1940's ....$1,200.00 +
Slot machine, Pace 8 Star,
1940's ....$1,000.00 +
Slot machine, Pace Bantam,
1920's ....$1,400.00 +
Slot machine, Mills Vest Pocket,
1930's ....$500.00 +
Card trimmer, brass....$1,000.00 +

Games

Game collecting probably began as an offshoot of the popular hobby of toy collecting, but has grown to be a well

An early skittles game table from the 1800's. $150.00-$200.00.

regarded hobby in its own right. Many games produced around the turn of the century or before are still being played today with little or no changes. Prices here are for games in good condition and in original boxes with no missing pieces.

Dominoes, Empire State
   building $10.00-12.00
"Have Gun Will Travel", T.V. series,
   1960's $10.00-15.00
Bicycle Race, McLoughlin Bros.,
   1890's $45.00-55.00
"Combat", T.V. series,
   1960's. $10.00-15.00
Dr. Busby, Ives,
   1840's $50.00-75.00
Dewey's Victory, Parker Brothers,
   1900 . . . . $30.00-40.00
Snow White, card game,
   1940's $3.00-5.00
Howdy Doody, card game,
   1950's $3.00-5.00
Nelly Bly Around the World,
   McLoughlin Bros.,
   1890's $65.00-75.00
Grocery Store, Parker Bros.,
   1880's $20.00-30.00
G-Men Clue, Whitman,
   1930's $15.00-17.00
Honey Bee, Milton Bradley,
   1913 . . . . $10.00-15.00
Farmer Jones Pigs, McLoughlin,
   early 1900's $25.00-30.00
Game of Banking, Parker Bros.,
   1880's $20.00-25.00
Authors, Sage Sons & Co.,
   1860's $40.00-50.00
Lexicon, Parker Bros.,
   1930's $3.00-5.00
Telegraph, McLoughlin,
   1880's $75.00-85.00
Indian, Milton Bradley,
   1920's $3.00-5.00

Mansion of Happiness, Ives,
   1840's $175.00-200.00
Touring, Parker Bros.,
   1920's $20.00-25.00
Fibber McGee & Mollie, Parker Bros.,
   1940's $10.00-15.00
Star Trek, 1960's $15.00-25.00

Glass Candlesticks

Nearly all of the glass houses in this country produced candlesticks. The many patterns, varieties and styles of the candlesticks produced through the years offer the collector a limitless source for collecting. Naturally, the more popular glass companies are the

Thumbprint and panel candlesticks from the 1930's. $50.00-$75.00.

Iris and Herringbone candlestick, $12.00-$14.00.

makers of the more popular candlesticks. More collectors are specializing in candlesticks and as the popularity increases, the value is also increasing.

Cambridge, Everglade,
2-holder $25.00-35.00
Cambridge, Twist,
8½ " $25.00-30.00
Cambridge, Crucifix . . . $25.00-30.00
Cambridge, Mt. Vernon,
8 " $60.00-65.00
Duncan, Daisy & Button,
hat, 2½ " $20.00-25.00
Fenton, Dolphin, 3½ " . $35.00-40.00
Fostoria, Baroque,
topaz, 4 " $18.00-20.00
Fostoria, Spiral Optic . . $10.00-12.00
Heisey, Trident, 5 " $50.00-60.00
Heisey, Colonial, 9 " . . . $65.00-75.00
Heisey, Lariat, dish,
2 " $10.00-15.00
Imperial, Drag Loop,
10¾ " $80.00-110.00
Imperial, Smithsonian,
5½ " $14.00-18.00

Imperial, Vinelf,
7½ " $28.00-34.00
Jeanette, Iris & Herringbone,
5½ " $12.00-14.00
McKee, Laurel, 4 " $18.00-22.00
Northwood, Hexagon Panels,
8½ " $40.00-45.00
Paden City, Nerva,
6 " $32.00-40.00
U.S. Glass, #15319,
Baluster, 8 " $35.00-40.00
Westmoreland, Spoke and Rim,
3½ " $14.00-16.00

Graniteware

Graniteware or enameled ware is the name given to enameled tinware. It was first manufactured in the United States in the 1870's, and was immediately popular. The majority of pieces have either a marbelized, shaded or spattered look and were produced in a variety of colors. Prices here are for pieces in good condition with minimal chips and no dents, holes or discoloration. Green, brown, or purple enameled ware pieces are somewhat

Graniteware coffee pots, $35.00-$45.00.

Lunch box, oval with 3 pieces, $95.00. The lunch box on the right is worth about $75.00.

A graniteware canister. $50.00.

Graniteware milk can. $35.00.

more valuable than the blue or grey pieces.

Bean pot, covered,
   grey $10.00-15.00
Stewing pan, covered,
   blue $15.00-30.00
Colander, blue $5.00-15.00

Teapot, goose neck spout,
   solid red $6.00-12.00
Wash basin, blue $8.00-10.00
Vegetable bowl, red . . . $10.00-15.00
Dishpan, green $12.00-16.00
Cooking pot, covered,
   1½ quart $7.00-12.00

Double boiler,
2 quart $12.00-16.00
Pie pan, 9",
grey $3.00-5.00
Milk dipper, 12" handle,
blue $5.00-10.00
Tea strainer, grey $5.00-10.00
Measuring cup, 1 pint,
grey $6.00-12.00
Fruit jar funnel, grey ...$5.00-10.00
Pudding mold, grey $5.00-10.00
Cake pan, angel food,
10", grey $12.00-15.00
Muffin pan, holds 8,
grey $10.00-15.00
Cornbread, 7"x12",
grey $3.00-6.00
Roasting pan, covered,
blue $12.00-20.00
Mug, brown $5.00-10.00

Guns

Guns are becoming more and more popular even though legislators are enacting stricter gun laws. The buyer should be aware of the legislation in his state before purchasing firearms and the seller should know the procedures and limitations under the law. Prices here are for used guns in excellent condition with no flaws.

Marlin Model A1
rifle $65.00-80.00
Remington Model 725 Magnum
rifle $400.00-500.00
Walther Model KKJ
rifle $300.00-375.00
Winchester Model 70 target
rifle..................$600.00+
Winchester Model 71
rifle $450.00-550.00
Savage Model 99C
rifle $175.00-250.00
Stevens Model 44
Ideal.............$250.00-300.00
Baikal IJ-12
shotgun $175.00-200.00
Baker Black Beauty Special
shotgun ....$500.00+
Beretta Asel
shotgun ....$625.00+
Browning Auto 5 Sweet Sixteen
shotgun ....$400.00+
Iver Johnson Champion
shotgun $65.00-75.00
Mossberg Model 385K
shotgun $65.00-100.00
Remington Model 3200 Field
shotgun ....$600.00+
Remington Model 10
shotgun ....$200.00+
Bayard 1908 pistol ..$100.00-200.00

High Standard Supermatic Special shotgun. $150.00-$175.00.

Remington Model 514 rifle. $50.00.

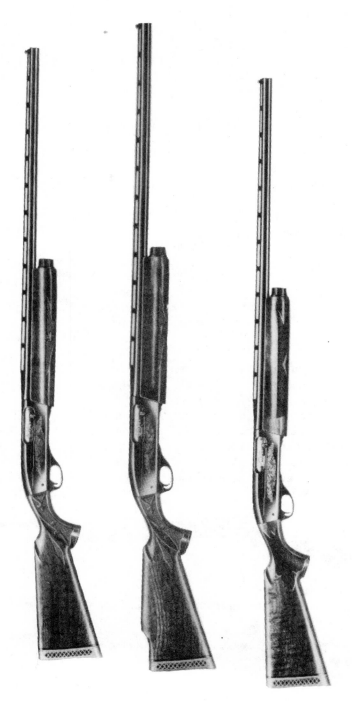

Remington Model 1100's. $250.00-350.00.

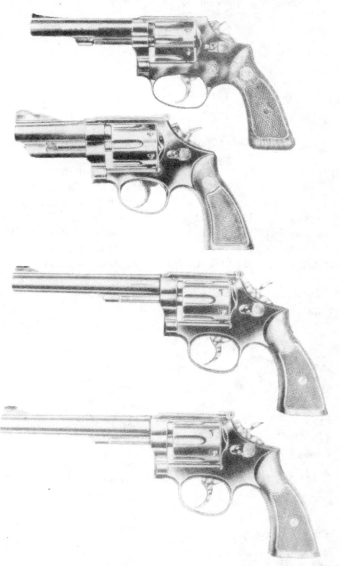

Smith & Wesson handguns. Model 31. $160.00; Model 27, $350.00; Model 17, $250.00; Model 48, $200.00.

Ruger Mark I Bull Barrel pistol. $100.00-$130.00.

Browning 25 Pocket
pistol $175.00-225.00
Colt Model N Pocket
pistol $200.00-250.00
Fiala Magazine pistol . . . . $600.00 +
H & R American
revolver $80.00-100.00

Hatpin Holders

As hatpins have become more popular,

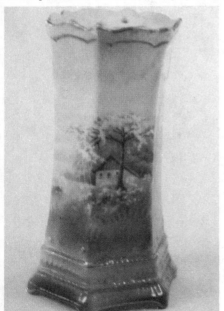

R.S. Prussia hatpin holder. $300.00-$400.00.

the colorful and attractive hatpin holders have also increased in interest. Though hatpin holders were made in a variety of materials including copper, gold, silver, carnival glass, cut glass, and china, the most popular holders were those of hand-painted porcelain. Many were part of dresser sets, all fashioned in the same material. Beware of reproduction hatpin holders, especially when buying the china type.

Royal Bayreuth . . . . $300.00 +
R.S. Prussia . . . . $150.00 +
Bavaria $25.00-50.00
Carnival glass . . . . $150.00 +
Kewpie, blue
Jasperware $175.00-200.00
Figural, pigs at the
pump $85.00-100.00
Figural, Art Deco
woman $85.00-100.00
Flow Blue $45.00-70.00
Figural owl $150.00-175.00
Satin glass $130.00-160.00

Hatpins

In the late 1800's as large ornate hats became popular, hatpins to hold them in place also became popular. Though the hatpin was used primarily to hold the hat in place, they were very useful

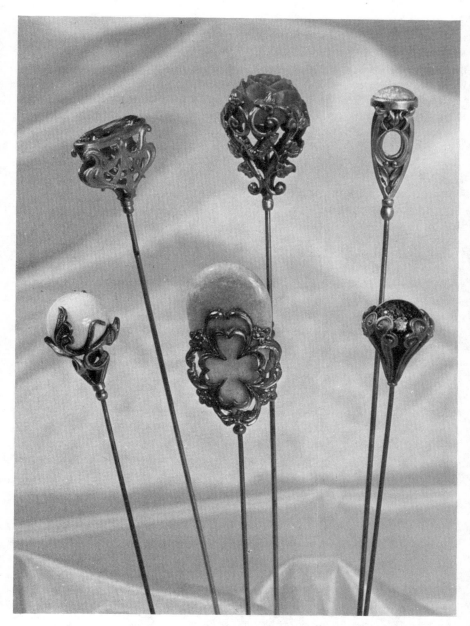

Hatpins, each worth about $35.00-$75.00.

for protection. Many are very ornate and contain precious metals and jewels and are in unusual figures and shapes. The popularity of hatpins declined around the first World War.

Mosaic $50.00-75.00

Figural animal $70.00-85.00

Cameo $85.00-100.00
Art Nouveau $80.00-100.00
Art Deco $50.00-60.00
Locket heads $50.00-75.00
Ivory $50.00-85.00
Shells $3.00-10.00
Rivited Jet $100.00-200.00
Vanity $100.00-200.00

Hull Pottery

The products of the Hull Pottery Company are increasing in value. Though the pieces slightly resemble some Roseville pottery and other popular pottery, they are still distinguishable and very colorful. Floral motifs were widely used by Hull and pastel color schemes are plentiful on the pottery.

Orchid, bookends, 7″,
  1930's $45.00-65.00
Iris, handled vase, 7″,

1940's $12.00-16.00
Dogwood, cornucopia,
  3¾″ $10.00-12.00
Poppy, wall pocket, 9″,
  1940's $30.00-40.00
Open Rose, hand vase,
  8½″ $25.00-30.00
Rosella, heart vase,
  6½″ $14.00-16.00
Wildflower, teapot,
  8″ $35.00-45.00
Water Lily, jardinier,
  8½″ $32.00-36.00
Bow Knot, flower pot & saucer,
  6½″ $18.00-24.00
Bow Knot, iron, wall pocket,
  6¼″ $25.00-30.00
Parchment and Pine, teapot,
  8″, 1950's $25.00-30.00
Sunglow, whisk broom, wall pocket,
  8¼″ $10.00-15.00
Woodland, ewer,
  5½″ $12.00-14.00

Hull Orchid vase. $30.00-$40.00. The ewer on the right is worth $45.00-$55.00.

154

The Magnolia Matte ewer is worth $40.00-$45.00 and the cornucopia is valued at $16.00-$20.00.

The Hull Wildflower vase is worth $25.00-$30.00. The ewer is worth $30.00-$40.00.

Cinderella Kitchenware, Blossom,
creamer, 4½ " $6.00-8.00
Tuba player figure,
5¾ " $8.00-10.00
Calla Lily, candlesticks,
2¼ " $20.00-25.00
Sueno Tulip, bud vase,
6 " $12.00-14.00
Magnolia Matte, double cornucopia,
12 " $25.00-30.00
Magnolia Gloss,
console bowl $22.00-26.00
Utility pitcher,
4¾ " $12.00-14.00

Hummel Figurines

The drawings of Sister Maria Innocentia Hummel of the Siessen Convet in Germany have come down to modern day collectors in the form of colorful, lifelike figures produced by the firm of W. Goebel. Hummel figures are very popular today with some rare examples bringing thousands of dollars. Though Hummel figures are still being produced, even new ones are very much in demand by American collectors. The older versions are usually more valuable and collectors are always on the lookout for rare versions and discontinued variations and markings. All genuine Hummel figures are marked, but the collector should beware of imitation figures in the same style.

Adoration, 6¼ ", stylized
bee mark $245.00-250.00
Angel Duet, 5½ ", stylized
bee mark $110.00-120.00
The Artist, 5¼ ",
any mark $100.00-200.00
Band Leader, 5 " $80.00-85.00
The builder, 5½ ". stylized
bee mark $160.00-200.00
Chick Girl, 4¼ ", full
bee mark $280.00-285.00
Cinderella, eyes closed, 5½ ", stylized
bee mark $140.00-150.00

Two examples of Hummel "Close Harmony" figurine, each worth $300.00.

The "For Father" figurine on the left has a crown trademark and is valued at $330.00. The one on the right has a full bee trademark and is worth $210.00.

Culprits, 6¼ ", full
   bee mark $200.00-225.00
Doctor, 4¾ ", full
   bee mark $150.00-170.00
Favorite Pet, 4¼ ", stylized
   bee mark $150.00-175.00
Feeding Time, 5½ " $80.00-90.00
Flower Vendor, 5½ ",
   any mark $100.00-150.00
Forest Shrine, 9 " $240.00-260.00
Globe Trotter, 5 ", full
   bee mark $185.00-220.00
Goose Girl, 4 ", stylized
   bee mark $100.00-120.00
Happiness, 4¾ ", full
   bee mark $130.00-145.00
Happy Pastine, 3¼ ", stylized
   bee mark $80.00-95.00
Homeward Bound, 5 ",
   any mark $165.00-220.00
Just Resting, 5 ", full
   bee mark $220.00-240.00

Little Cellist, 6 ", stylized
   bee mark $140.00-150.00
Little Gabriel, 5 ", full
   bee mark $140.00-165.00
Max and Moritz, 5¼ ", stylized
   bee mark $120.00-135.00
Mother's Helper, 5 " . . . $70.00-85.00
Out of Danger, 6¼ ", stylized
   bee mark $160.00-180.00
The Photographer, 4¾ ", full
   bee mark $250.00-270.00
Playmates, 4 ", full
   bee mark $190.00-200.00
Postman, 5¼ ", full
   bee mark $200.00-225.00
Puppy Lover, 5 ", stylized
   bee mark $100.00-125.00
Retreat to Safety, 4 ", full
   bee mark $160.00-180.00
Sensitive Hunter, 4¾ ", stylized
   bee mark $100.00-120.00
Serenade, 4¾ ", full

Hummel figurine "Volunteers".

Hummel figurine ''The Runaway''.

bee mark $130.00-150.00
Shepherd Boy, 5½", full
bee mark $200.00-225.00
Shining Light, 2¾". . . . $30.00-40.00
Signs of Spring, 4", stylized
bee mark $115.00-130.00
Singing Lesson, 2¾", full
bee mark $150.00-175.00
Sister, 4¾", full
bee mark $120.00-140.00
Skier, 5¼", stylized
bee mark $140.00-155.00
Smart Little Sister,
4¾" $80.00-90.00
Soldier Boy, 6", stylized
bee mark $100.00-125.00
Spring Cheer, 5" $40.00-55.00
Star Gazer, 4¾", stylized
bee mark $120.00-140.00
Sweet Music, 5¼", stylized
bee mark $120.00-140.00
To Market, 4", full
bee mark $180.00-195.00
Umbrella Boy, 5", stylized
bee mark $450.00-500.00
Umbrella Girl, 4¾", stylized
bee mark $450.00-500.00
Village Boy, 4", full
bee mark $80.00-95.00
Visiting An Invalid, 5". $70.00-90.00
Volunteers, 5", full
bee mark $250.00-275.00
Waiter, 6", stylized
bee mark $100.00-125.00
Wash Day, 5¼", stylized
bee mark $150.00-170.00
Wayside Devotion, 7½", stylized
bee mark $220.00-240.00
Wayside Harmony, 3¾", stylized
bee mark $95.00-105.00
Weary Wonderer, 6", full
bee mark $200.00-225.00
We Congratulate, 4", full
bee mark $260.00-285.00
Which Hand?, 5¼", stylized

bee mark $110.00-115.00
Worship, 5", full bee
mark $200.00-225.00

Indian Artifacts

Indian tools and relics can be found all over the United States and the type of relics found can tell much about the history of a particular area. These items are collected more for their historic appeal than their monetary worth. When these tools and relics are uncovered, a record should be kept as to location. This adds to the value and interest of the item. Tools and relics that exhibit good craftsmanship and detail are the most desirable. Geographic boundaries contribute greatly to the value of these items.

Boys jacket, floral beadwork, beadwork, buckskin, 1880's $350.00-375.00
Possibles bag, 17"x23", beaded, Sioux or Cheyenne, 1890's$650.00-700.00
Leggings & vest, Plains Indian, 1880's $800.00-850.00
Baby cap, hide with beads, Plains Indian $275.00-300.00
Arm band, Sioux $20.00-30.00
Hair roach, deer hide and porcupine quills, 1900's $50.00-60.00
Pipe bag, 7"x33", beaded and quilled, early 1900's $450.00-500.00
Child's moccasins, beadwork and quillwork, 1880's . . $250.00-265.00
Fleshing tool, wood with metal blade, 1850's $40.00-45.00

Flint blade with serrated edges. $10.00-$15.00.

Stemmed point blade. $20.00-$30.00.

Iron pipe axe. $600.00 and up.

War club, rawhide wrapped handle,
Sioux $125.00-150.00
Cradleboard, beaded buckskin,
sunshade, Paiute . . $250.00-275.00
Breastplate, leather thongs, bone
tubes, beaded,
1900's $650.00-700.00
Knife sheath, rawhide, 6½ ″, Western
Plains $40.00-50.00
Painted bow, sinew-strung, Hopi,
1890's $75.00-100.00
Hair ties, beadwork & featherdown,
brass dangles $20.00-30.00

Jewelry

Antique jewelry has increased steadily in value over the past few years. This
is due largely to the amount of gold,
silver and gems involved. As the prices
of modern jewelry continue to climb,
people seem to be turning to antique
jewelry, causing prices to rise more.
Because valuable metals and gems are
present in jewelry, the prices are rather
unstable. Prices can fluctuate greatly
in a very short period of time. Jewelry
can be a sound investment if only for
the amount of valuable elements
involved.

Cross, Etruscan, hollow gold, applied
design, 1890's $300.00-350.00

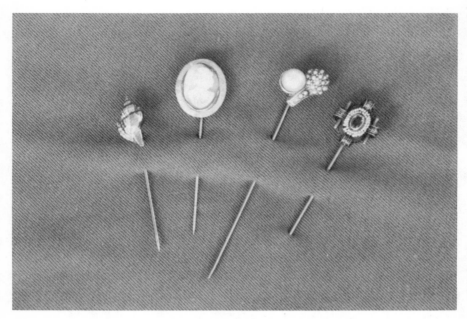

Stick pins: conch shell, 18k gold, $135.00; cameo, gold wash, $40.00; pearl, seed pearl cluster, $25.00; amythest, gold filled, $50.00.

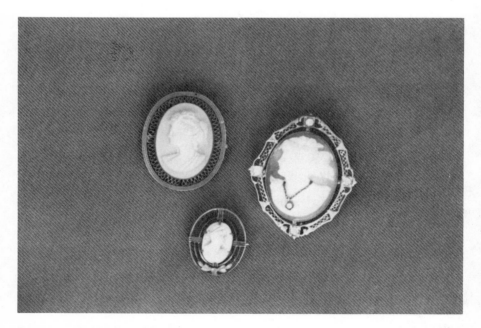

Cameo, shell gold plate filigree, $40.00; cameo, shell, small, $30.00; cameo, shell, 14k gold, diamonds, $165.00.

A lapel pin, topaz, pearl shell. $30.00.

An Art Nouveau silver plate buckle. $20.00.

Combs of tortoise shell. $40.00-$55.00.

Cameo, shell, gold filled, $85.00; cameo, shell, iris, $95.00; cameo, shell, sterling, $95.00.

164

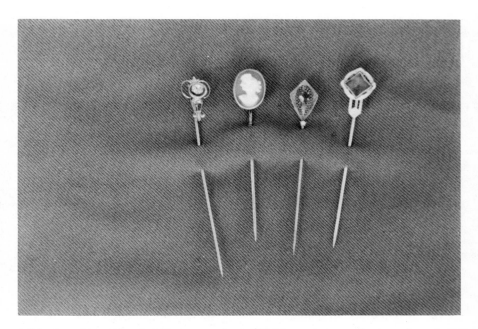

Stick pins, rhinestone, Art Nouveau mount, $30.00; cameo, amythest, seed pearl, 10k gold, $20.00; sterling, pink stone, $25.00.

Cameo, shell, 14k gold frame,
floral $400.00-450.00
Brooch, 18k gold, amethyst center,
4 diamonds $450.00-500.00
Necklace, Bohemian garnets, gold
chain, 1890's $200.00-250.00
Brooch, bird, sterling silver,
4½ " $50.00-75.00
Necklace, Art Deco, Egyptian
style, glass drops,
cobalt beads $150.00-200.00
Choker, gilt, mesh with tassels,
1940's $15.00-20.00
Brooch, moth, gold wash, simulated
stones $30.00-35.00
Bracelet, cinnabar and filigree,
sterling silver $120.00-125.00
Necklace, gilt & enamel, Venetian
red glass beads $30.00-35.00
Lavaliere, 18k gold pendant, 14K
chain, 1850's $150.00-175.00
Brooch, dragonfly,

glass stone $20.00-25.00
Beads, 2 color, amber &
gold beads $200.00-250.00
Bracelet, Rhodium,
rhinestone $100.00-125.00
Stud buttons, 10k gold,
engraved $20.00-25.00
Fob, sterling silver, skull,
1900 . . . . $30.00-35.00
Bracelet, hollow gold tubing,
blue enamel,
half pearls $500.00-600.00
Bar pin, engraved sterling,
imitation jade $15.00-20.00
Necklace, Carnelian & marcasite
in sterling, France,
1920's $100.00-150.00
Earrings, sterling, Bohemian
glass with marcasites . $50.00-75.00

Kitchen Antiques
Anything used in, or pertaining to, the

This washboard has glass ridges and a pine frame and is worth $45.00.

kitchen is considered a kitchen collectible. This is a wide ranging category that overlaps into other areas of collecting. Most of these items are used solely for decoration. Many pieces, though, such as cabinets, tables, and crockery are being used as functional items. The collector should beware of reproductions in this area.

Ladle, brass, iron
    handle $70.00-80.00
Chopping knife, maple handle,
    1880's $35.00-45.00
Table, pine, center

drawer . . . . $200.00 +
Cherry pitter, iron,
    1920's $30.00-35.00
Dough roller, maple . . . $30.00-35.00
Lemon squeezer, maple,
    1850's-1870's $55.00-70.00
Sad iron $8.00-20.00
Sieve, horsehair and
    wood $75.00-85.00
Pie safe, walnut,
    star tins . . . . $350.00 +
Sugar bucket, eyelet
    hoops $185.00-215.00
Tea kettle, cast iron . . . $60.00-70.00
Apple peeler, cast iron,

1900's $60.00-70.00
Kraut slicer, wood,
   iron blades $70.00-100.00
Pudding mold, copper . $50.00-70.00
Tea kettle, copper,
   wood handle $100.00-115.00
Cookie cutter, tin,
   horse $50.00-75.00
Muffin pan, iron,
   1880's $40.00-50.00
Apple butter kettle, copper,
   1880's $50.00-65.00
Cornbread mold, iron,
   corn shape $15.00-25.00
Cake mold, iron $40.00-50.00

Lamps, Electric

The transition to a clean, less trouble-some fuel, from the open flame type was welcomed in America. Thomas Edison's patent of the light bulb made it possible to have a more evenly distributed light with only a minimum of preparation and maintenance. Although lighting fixtures have chang-ed outwardly to suit the changing tastes of the public, the lamps of to-day are really not far removed from

This tin cake baker with a sliding lid is worth about $60.00.

The muffin pan on the left is worth about $10.00. The pie pan at right is valued at about $16.00.

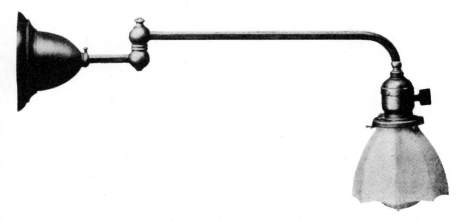

An extension wall lamp. $115.00-$135.00.

An electric lamp with art glass shade. $190.00-$215.00.

the early types. Any signed Tiffany lamp can bring up to $10,000 and more depending on type and condition. Any Art Nouveau or Art Deco lamps are popular among collectors.

Metal stand, 4-sided art glass
  shade $350.00-450.00
Desk lamp, brass
  gooseneck $75.00-90.00

Gilt urn base, satin ball
  shade $350.00-420.00
Brass base with figural dragons,
  tulip shade . . . . $1,000.00 +
Desk lamp, brass tube,
  adjustable $180.00-235.00
Hanging, oak mission, triangular art
  glass shade $200.00-285.00
Rayo, painted shade . $100.00-125.00
Pewter base, art glass

168

Two oak and art glass lamps. Each is valued at about $200.00.

shade $275.00-300.00
Gone with the Wind, embossed
lions $200.00-250.00
Gone with the Wind, floral, pink &
green . . . . $300.00+
Hanging, brass, art glass shade with
fruit design . . . . $1,000.00+
Hanging, brass chain, art glass shade
with grapes design . . . $1,000.00+
Table lamp, "Tiffany" style, brass
with art glass shade$350.00-425.00
Wall lamp, brass sconce, satin ball
shade $150.00-175.00
Hanging, brass chain, curved pink art
glass shade, tassels . . . $1,000.00+

Lamps, Oil

Oil lamps have been made in many
materials, but the majority found today are made of glass. Oil lamps rely
on an open flame for light, and have
been so popular that they were sold
long after electricity was an establish-
ed form of lighting. Cut and pattern
glass lamps made before the turn of the
century are very popular, especially the
vase or "Gone with the Wind" lamps.

A Little Jewel miniature lamp. $140.00.

169

A pewter oil lamp. $45.00.

This Fostoria green milk glass lamp is worth about $175.00.

A Fairy lamp with molded floral design worth about $70.00.

The collector should use caution when buying oil lamps because reproductions are available.

Star $50.00-60.00
Betty lamp, iron .... $175.00+
Gone with the Wind, red satin
glass .... $525.00+
Glass, Diamond Bead &
Shield $185.00-200.00
Miners lamp, tin,
wicked spout $35.00-45.00

Limoges

Hard base porcelain was produced by many factories around Limoges, France. The high quality pieces made form the mid 1800's to about 1930 are of interest to antique collectors. Many pieces are artist signed and all are beautiful. There is quite a selection of this porcelain around but nearly all carries a premium price.

Vase, 9″, roses, artist signed,
"Skeen" $65.00-90.00
Tankard, 15″. grapes, artist signed
"Loufall" $375.00-425.00
Bon bon bowl, 7″x4″, "Venice",
1890's $30.00-40.00
Hand mirror, 9″x5″, handpainted
floral $35.00-50.00
Cachepot, 7″, roses, artist signed,
"M.K.O.L." $125.00-160.00
Picture frame, 7″x10″, scalloped
border $110.00-135.00
Berry bowl, 9½″, blueberries,
signed, "Schmidt
1902" $55.00-75.00
Cake plate, 10½″, embossed
floral $45.00-60.00
Chocolate set, signed,
"F. Howard" $295.00-325.00
Cider pitcher, 6½″, floral decor,
signed, "A.M.K." . $95.00-125.00
Ewer, 12″, floral
decor $70.00-90.00
Egg plate, scalloped border,
handpainted $55.00-70.00

A Bristol miniature lamp. $70.00.

Glass, square font, oval & panel stem,
pewter collar $105.00-115.00
Bedside lamp, brass, pedestal, glass
chimney $70.00-75.00
Tin petticoat lamp, kerosene,
1860's $300.00-350.00
Finger lamp, kerosene, brass cap and
burner $35.00-40.00
Glass, hexagonal base, diamond
pattern font $40.00-65.00
Whale oil lamp, pewter,
brass collar & double
spout burner...... $100.00-120.00
Wall lamp, tin with glass chimney,
late 1800's $240.00-280.00
Grease lamp, wrought iron, twisted
hanger $100.00-120.00
Whale oil lamp, tin, double wick
burner $125.00-150.00
Student lamp, brass,
double .... $325.00+
Peglamp, Diamond &

Limoges oyster plate.

Limoges plates.

Fish set, 25″ platter & 21 plates,
  handpainted $600.00-900.00
Oyster plate, 8¼″, square,
  handpainted $75.00-90.00
Ice cream bowl,
  floral $140.00-175.00
Basket, 8″,
  embossed floral . . .$110.00-145.00

Tray, 7″x6″, floral
  decor $165.00-195.00
Trinket box, heart shape,
  woman & owl. $110.00-135.00
Dresser set, 5 pieces, handpainted
  floral $175.00-215.00
Tankard, 14″,
  plums $285.00-315.00

Limoges art vase.

Limoges occupational mug.

Locks

Locks of wood crossbars were used in Egypt and biblical cities. Since that time, locksmithing has evolved to our present day sophisticated lock mechanisms. Old locks and keys are of interest to collectors if they are in good condition and working order. Railroad locks are especially popular.

A group of 4-lever locks.

A group of 6-lever locks.

Pin tumbler, Reese,
    "USN" $7.00-15.00
Pin tumbler, Fraim Slaymaker,
    "Winchester" $40.00-60.00
8 lever, Corbin,
    Samson $7.00-15.00

Ward lock, "S & Co." . $7.00-15.00
Ward lock, wrought iron,
    "W.W. & Co." $15.00-20.00
Ward lock, Conqueror . . . $4.00-5.00
Ward lock, Master, Ace . $4.00-5.00
Ward lock, S.B. Co.,

sprocket	$20.00-25.00
Wafer, Lion	$4.00-5.00
3 lever lock, Fraim, Anchor	$7.00-15.00
6 lever, Keen Kutter	$40.00-50.00
Pin tumbler, S.O. Co., Best	$7.00-15.00
Combination, U.S. Customs	$40.00-50.00
Pin tumbler, Corbin, tire lock	$40.00-50.00
Blacksmith, screw key lock	$25.00-30.00

Magazines

Old magazines give the collector a look at how life was in the past. The cost of magazines in good condition is increasing, especially those before 1920, World War II issues, and some issues with special historical significance. There is a variety of magazines available to the collector on many subjects. Discontinued publications are very popular and demand good prices but early issues of Playboy are probably the most sought after magazines with the December 1953 issue worth over $500.00.

The American, any before 1935	$2.00-4.00
Better Homes & Gardens, any before 1950	$2.00-5.00
Better Homes & Gardens, 1950's-1960's	50¢-$1.00
Colliers, before 1930's	$3.00-10.00
Esquire, 1930's	$7.00-15.00

A 1919 *Colliers* worth about $4.00-$10.00.

T.V. Guide **magazines from the early 1970's. $1.00-$3.00.**

A wartime issue of *Esquire.*

Esquire,
1940's-1950's $3.00-10.00

Family Cirlce, 1930's $3.00-5.00

Good Housekeeping,
1920's-1930's $3.00-5.00

Hot Rod,
1940's & 1950's $5.00-10.00

Ladies Home Journal,
1880's $5.00-10.00

Ladies Home Journal,
1930's $3.00-7.00

Life, Volume 1, #1,
November 23, 1936 ..$50.00-70.00

McCalls, before 1950's ...$3.00-5.00

New Yorker,
 1940's or 1950's $1.00-2.00
Playboy, Volume 1, #1,
 December 1953
 (Marilyn Monroe) . $500.00-800.00
Playboy, 1950's $50.00-150.00
Seventeen,

 1950's or 1960's $2.00-3.00
Silver Screen, 1950's $2.00-3.00
T.V. Guide,
 1950's-1960's $3.00-5.00
Time, 1920's or 1930's . . . $1.00-2.00

Majolica

Majolica is a tin glaze pottery that

Majolica vases.

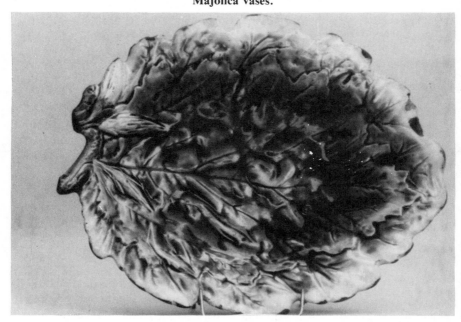

A Majolica leaf bowl showing the style of figural items produced.

derives its name from early pottery designed in Europe. The collectible Majolica, made by many companies, is many times figural and flowery in style and is nearly always rich in color. There is a good selection on the market to fit many tastes.

Oyster plate $30.00-50.00
Teapot $40.00-60.00
Covered tureen $50.00-65.00
Covered humidor $50.00-100.00
Inkwell $35.00-50.00
Butter pat $15.00-25.00
Tureen, animal or
    bird $50.00-75.00
Vase $10.00-35.00
Syrup pitcher $25.00-35.00
Water pitcher $30.00-40.00

Marbles

The game of marbles is one of the oldest in history. Over the years many types of marbles have been made: sulphides, swirls, stone, crockery, china, clay, and other materials. Marbles are popular with collectors and because of the bright, cheerful colors they make attractive displays. The most sought after marble is probably the sulphide. The large sulphides with double figures will easily bring over $100.00 from a marble collector.

Stone Marbles

	1/2"	3/4"	1"
Common	$3.00	$3.50	$7.00
Agate	$15.00	$7.50	$12.50
Tiger Eye	$17.50	$12.50	$27.50

Unglazed China

Lines	$1.50	$1.25	$2.00
Bullseye	$1.75	$1.50	$2.25
Leaves	$1.75	$2.00	$2.00

Sulphides

Double figures	$100.00-125.00
Animals	$50.00-75.00
Train	$50.00-75.00
Color figures	$100.00-125.00

Swirls

Banded	$6.50	$3.00	$12.50
Split Core	$4.75	$4.50	$12.50
Candle	$4.50	$5.00	$12.50
Candy	$4.50	$4.75	$12.50
Joseph	$12.50	$7.50	$17.50

Glazed China

Lines	$2.00	$3.00	$4.75
Bullseye	$2.00	$1.75	$3.00
Leaves	$2.00	$2.00	$3.00
Stars	$3.00	$2.75	$5.50
Flowers	$3.25	$3.25	$5.50

Crockery or Bennington

Brown	$1.00	$1.00	$2.50
Speckled	$1.25	$1.50	$3.00
Blue	$1.00		$2.75
Odd color	$2.00	$2.00	$4.00

Akro Agate marbles in the original box. There is even a knee pad included to save wear and tear on the pant legs. The original box full of marbles is valued at about $50.00.

McCoy Pottery

McCoy Pottery has become increasingly popular with collectors in recent years, with some of the more rare handpainted pieces selling for hun-

McCoy cookie jars. The Indian is from the mid 1950's and is worth $85.00-$95.00. The tipi from the late 1950's is valued at $65.00-$75.00.

McCoy Wrenhouse from the 1950's is worth $20.00-$25.00. The Dalmation cookie jar is valued at $60.00-$65.00.

dreds of dollars. The most abundant products of McCoy are the popular cookie jars but the most desirable pieces are the handpainted pieces from the early 1900's. As the rare types increase in value, all kinds of McCoy pottery are being grabbed up by collectors.

Indian cookie jar,
    1950's $85.00-95.00
Uncle Sam planter,
    1940's $10.00-15.00
Clown cookie jar,
    1940's $10.00-15.00
Mother Goose cookie jar,
    1940's $35.00-40.00

Early McCoy pottery. Top row: Vase, $100.00; ewer, $200.00; vase, $100.00. Middle row: Vase, $175.00; vase, $100.00; vase, $175.00. Bottom row: Vase, $35.00-50.00; experimental vase, $300.00-500.00; vase, $25.00-35.00.

McCoy Pottery pieces. $3.00-10.00 each.

A globe cookie jar from the late 1950's is valued at $22.00-$28.00. The Rooster on the right is worth about the same.

Loy-Nel-Art, 2 handled vase, 1905,
8″ $100.00-125.00
Elephant cookie jar,
1940's $25.00-35.00
Hen on nest cookie jar,
1950's $20.00-25.00
Double duck and egg planter,
1940's $6.00-8.00
Discus thrower, planter,
1940's $12.00-15.00
Umbrella wall pocket,
1950's $8.00-10.00
Zebra planter, 1950's ... $8.00-10.00
Ivy tea set $35.00-40.00
Lamp base, whaling
man $25.00-35.00
Bananas cookie jar,
1950's $20.00-25.00
Christmas tree cookie jar,
1950's $80.00-90.00
Rooster cookie jar,
1950's $22.00-28.00
Panther planter,
1950's $7.00-10.00
Bear cookie jar,
1940's $15.00-18.00

Chipmunk cookie jar,
1950's $35.00-40.00
Puppy in basket cookie jar,
1950's $15.00-18.00

Medical Collectibles

Medical collectibles are fast becoming of major interest in the area of collecting, especially to those that have some interest in the medical field. Although many of the items considered medical collectibles were actually used by doctors, dentists, nurses or hospitals, this is not the rule. Many, in fact, are pharmaceutical items from druggists and drug stores or items sold as home remedies or cures. Anything from bottled pills to electric shocking machines is popular including the "quack" pieces that were originally sold promising miraculous cures.

Petit's Spiral Tourniquet, brass &
webbing, 1860's $50.00-60.00
Straight-edge forceps .. $30.00-50.00
Artery forceps, steel ... $15.00-25.00

Pocket scales, used by physicians in the 1880's. $65.00.

A Vapo-Cresolene lamp. $50.00-$100.00.

An early pill press. $40.00-$45.00.

Pocket medicine case, leather,
9 bottles $20.00-25.00
Surgical knife, sterling
silver $50.00-55.00
Ear trumpet, brass and ivory,
1860's $150.00-175.00
Eye cup, cobalt blue
glass $10.00-12.00
Medicine spoon, sterling silver,
velvet lined case . . . . . $1,000.00 +
Catalog, Bausch & Lomb, optical
equipment, 1900 . . . . $20.00-25.00
Microscope, brass body, iron base,
wood case, 1860's . $250.00-450.00
Dental mouth mirror, carved mother
of pearl handle $60.00-75.00
Doctor's bag, leather,
black $50.00-75.00
Surgical needle holder, in steel
casing, 1880's $20.00-25.00
Pocket surgical set, ivory handled
scalpels, leather
case $150.00-200.00
Tracheotomy set, 3-piece cased
set $150.00-175.00
Hot water bottle, chrome plated,
1900's $5.00-10.00
Balance, wood case with marble top,
pan scales $75.00-100.00
Dental chair, walnut & oak,
upholstered back &
seat . . . . $600.00 +

Hand drill, ivory, socket
handle $150.00-200.00
Tablet press, 1890's . . . $10.00-12.00

Metal Molds

Molds for ice cream, chocolate, barley
sugar, and cake are usually figural and
made from pewter and other metals.
Bunnies are plentiful but still bring
good prices as do Santas, and other
holiday themes.

Rooster, 11½ ", pewter, ice
cream $300.00-400.00
Cornucopia, tin washed copper, ice
cream $20.00-25.00
Turkey, pewter, ice
cream $35.00-45.00
Witch on broom, pewter, ice
cream $65.00-75.00
Crown, pewter, ice
cream $25.00-45.00
Rabbit, boxing, chocolate, clamp
type $45.00-55.00
Three rabbits, hinged and banded,
chocolate $30.00-40.00
Three Santas, hinged and clamped,
chocolate $65.00-75.00
Pencil, chocolate, 8½ ". $25.00-30.00
Indian copper, chocolate,
7½ " $25.00-35.00
Drum, 3-piece, pewter, ice

A mold in the shape of an engine and coal car. $70.00-$75.00 each.

A lying rabbit mold worth about $30.00-$45.00.

An unusual two-piece boxing rabbit mold. $45.00-$55.00.

cream $65.00-75.00
Rose and leaves, pewter, ice
   cream $45.00-55.00
Santa, 2-piece, cast aluminum,
   cake, 12″ $75.00-85.00
Hobby horse, pewter, ice
   cream $65.00-75.00
Worn shoe, pewter, ice
   cream $30.00-50.00
Hershey bar, flat, chocolate,
   from factory $10.00-20.00
Heart, 9″, chocolate . . . $55.00-65.00
Snowman, 4″,
   chocolate $45.00-50.00
Grapes, pewter, ice

cream $35.00-45.00
3 hens on nests, barley
sugar $15.00-20.00

Military Collectibles

War and the military has an unusual fascination for many collectors. Items used by any Army, Navy, or Air Force is of interest but those connected with the Civil War, World War I, and World War II are usually more valuable. Nazi collectibles generally demand very high prices. Beware of reproduction and replica Civil War relics.

Civil War
Cavalry officer hat with cord,
CSA $150.00-200.00
Cannonball tongs,
iron $50.00-75.00
Cap, U.S. officers, embroidered
wreath $100.00-120.00

Cannon ramrod, wood, brass,
and iron $45.00-60.00
Enlisted man's
epaulettes $100.00-150.00

WWI
Poster, "I Want You", Uncle Sam
by J.M. Flagg . . . . $600.00+
Officer's sword and
scabbard $100.00-125.00
Infantry leggins, brown
leather $10.00-20.00
Knapsack, U.S.A., canvas,
leather straps $15.00-20.00
Cartridge box, tin $3.00-5.00

WWII
German Navy Captain's
hat . . . . $500.00+
Luftwaffe Summer hat,
officer's . . . . $200.00+
Poster, "Jap, You're Next!",
Flagg . . . . $100.00″
Helmet, U.S. $25.00-35.00

A Nazi Navy captain's hat. $500.00.

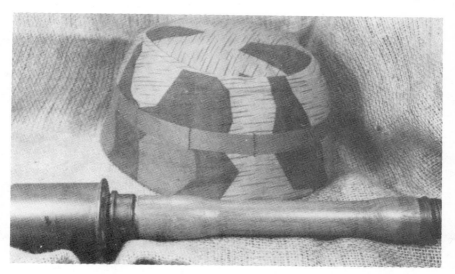

The World War II German paratrooper helmet is worth about $225.00. The camouflage cover is worth another $200.00. The hand grenade will bring as much as $60.00-$65.00.

U.S. Field manual $2.50-5.00
Aerial photography manual,
   1941, U.S. $3.00-5.00
German Army dagger, damascus
   blade . . . . $2,000.00+
Poster, "Attack, Attack, Attack--
   Buy War Bonds" . . . $50.00-60.00
Afrikakorps helmet,
   steel $175.00-200.00
German hand grenade . $65.00-75.00

Movie Memorabilia

Things connected with movies, especially large posters, are attractive to view and popular to collect. In addition to posters, collectors look for movie stills, lobby cards, tabloid heralds, books, magazines, etc. Anything related is popular and generally, the more popular the movie, the more valuable the collectibles.

The Ten Commandments, souvenir
   book, 20 pages $25.00-30.00

Wizard of Oz lobby
   card $50.00-75.00
Gone With The Wind, paperback
   book, 1940 . . . . $15.00-25.00
All About Eve, poster,
   27"x41" $40.00-50.00
Sinbad The Sailor, press book,
   1947 . . . . $15.00-18.00
Wizard of Oz, poster,
   27"x41" . . . . $300.00+
Dawn Patrol, book,
   1930 . . . . $10.00-12.00
Easy Rider, pressbook,
   1969 . . . . $8.00-10.00
Golddiggers of 1933, lobby card,
   11"x14" $75.00-100.00
The Mummy, insert,
   14"x36" . . . . $500.00+
Gigi, 1958, souvenir
   book $10.00-12.00
Mr. Roberts, press book,
   1955 . . . . $12.50-15.00
Maltese Falcon, poster,
   27"x41" $175.00-200.00
Is Paris Burning?, press book,

An edition of *Screen Guide* from the 1940's.

1966 .... $12.00-15.00
Casablanca, lobby card,
  11 "x14 " $40.00-55.00

Nautical Collectibles

The lure of the sea has long been a fascination for young and old. Anything to do with shipping is considered collectible, whether it's salt water or river navigation. Almost any era is popular, but especially good are sailing, whaling and wartime items.

Timetable, Ocean Steamship Co.,
  Feb. 1893 .... $5.00-10.00
Booklet, *Marine Engines by Kermath*,

1940's, specs, blueprints,
  etc. $3.00-4.00
Launch brochure, Queen Elizabeth,
  1938 .... $125.00-150.00
Bill of Lading, Schooner Henry Curtis, Boston,
  1840's $15.00-20.00
Invoice, Schooner Victory, Boston,
  1819 .... $10.00-20.00
Plans, two matted, Plum Beach Light Station, Rhode Island,
  1890's $70.00-80.00
Whaler, ship owner's ledger, 1815-18,
  New Bedford, MA ..... $350.00 +
Broadside, "NY to SF in 8½ days",
  7x9 .... $100.00-125.00

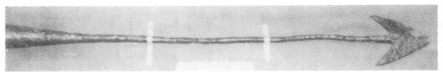

A double flue Artic harpoon from the early 1800's. $225.00.

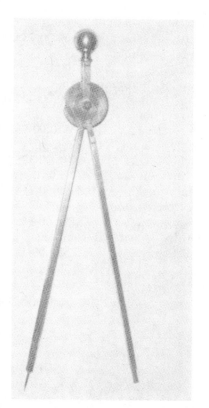

Mariner's dividers from the early 1800's. $70.00.

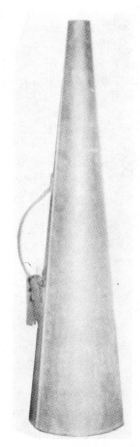

This mate's horn is from the 1830's and is worth about $50.00.

Life preserver, "doughnut", "S.S. John P. Poe", canvas on cork $80.00-100.00

Steamboat engineer's wrench $25.00-30.00

Belaying pin, carved from oak $40.00-50.00

Whale block pulley, early 1800's $125.00-150.00

Arctic harpoon, forged iron, 1800's $225.00-250.00

Mariner's dividers, brass, 1810 . . . . $75.00-100.00

Book, *Under Sail*, 1919 . . . . $12.00-15.00

Ship's bell, brass with clapper & bracket $75.00-100.00

Seaman's chest, pine with rope handles, approx. 4′ long $50.00-100.00

Sail maker's needle case, ivory, 6″ $75.00-100.00

Ship's chronometer, rosewood & brass . . . . $800.00+

Sextant, brass with case . . $425.00+

Nippon

Handpainted pieces of porcelain imported into this country from Japan from 1890 to 1921 were marked "Nippon". These colorful inexpensive

This Nippon vase is worth $325.00-$425.00.

pieces have now become quite popular and many have become relatively expensive. There are many examples and varieties available to the collector.

Humidor, 5½", American Indian
decoration $500.00-625.00
Vase, elephant molded in relief,
8" . . . . $1,200.00+
Stein, desert scene, man on camel,
7" $325.00-450.00
Humidor, fox hunt scene,
7¼" $475.00-600.00
Ashtray, Egyptian Pharaoh
decoration, 4" $90.00-125.00
Tankard, 11", 4-4" mugs, deer
decoration $900.00-1,200.00
Hanging plate, black man playing
banjo, 7¾" $250.00-325.00

Cake plate, windmill, scene,
10¾" $160.00-235.00
Figural penguin ashtray,
6"x5" $700.00-850.00
Humidor, lion decoration,
5½" $400.00-475.00
Ashtray, lion
decoration $70.00-95.00
Hanging plaque, 11", dogs in
field $275.00-375.00
Shaving mug, 4",
landscape $120.00-155.00
Egg server, floral
decoration $125.00-155.00
Tea tile, woman with umbrella,
5½" $35.00-55.00

A 14" covered urn. $600.00-$800.00.

The Nippon vases at the top are worth $125.00-280.00; the two at the bottom are worth about $150.00-200.00.

Nippon ashtrays, $85.00-125.00.

Nippon hanging plaques with desert scenes. $235.00-$300.00.

Occupied Japan

Following World War II anything made for export in Japan during the American Occupation had to be marked either "Occupied Japan" or "Made in Occupied Japan". Since this occupation lasted only about 8 years, the items manufactured and exported at that time have become collectors items. Many products were made during this period including those manufactured of glass, celluloid, metal, paper, and wood. Because there is such an abundance of available collectibles, the value of Occupied Japan is relatively low. But as more collectors begin to surface, the collectibles are already increasing in value.

Ashtray, metal with trolley,
    San Francisco $15.00-20.00
Cologne bottle & tray, blue translucent
    glass $20.00-25.00
Cigarette lighter, gun
    shape $10.00-12.00
Cucoo clock, wood . . $100.00-125.00
Aquarium figure,
    mermaid $12.00-15.00

Wind chimes, glass $20.00-25.00
Jockey & racehorse, metal
    figure $12.00-15.00
Paper fan $4.00-5.00
Toby mug, skull $12.00-15.00
Mug, cowboy handle . . $12.00-15.00
Tray, lacquerware,
    five-part $50.00-55.00
Candy dish, leaf and grapes,
    metal $10.00-12.00
Cigarette dispenser, piano,
    metal $18.00-20.00
Lamp, Wedgwood
    style $50.00-55.00

Occupied Japan clock. $35.00-$45.00.

195

Occupied Japan figurines in the Hummel style. These figures are worth about $12.00-$20.00 each.

Small tray, metal, St. Louis
   Zoo souvenir $2.00-3.00
Salt & pepper set,
   tomatoes $4.00-5.00
Salt & pepper set,
   windmills $20.00-25.00
Zebra planter $4.00-6.00
Ice bucket & tongs,
   lacquerware $20.00-25.00
Fishbowl ornament, hanging
   cat $6.00-8.00

Paper Dolls

Dolls of paper, either complete booklets or magazine pages are highly collectible. The dolls here are booklets and priced for complete uncut examples. Celebrities and dolls from movies are the most popular paper dolls at this time, but all types are collectible.

Saalfield

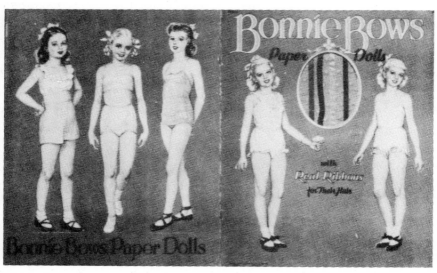

Bonnie Bows **paperdolls from 1953. $5.00.**

Pink Prom Twins **from 1956. $5.00.**

This Esther Williams paperdoll book from 1950 is worth about $35.00.

Bettina And Her Playmate Rosalie,
  1930's $25.00-30.00
Walter Lantz Cartoon Stars,
  1960's $10.00-12.00
Hollywood Fashion Dolls,
  1939 . . . . $10.00-12.00
Daisy Mae and Li'l Abner,
  1941 . . . . $20.00-25.00
Army and Navy Wedding Party,
  1940's *$20.00-25.00*
Ozzie and Harriet,
  1954 . . . . $20.00-25.00

Prince Valiant and Princess Aleta,
  1950's $15.00-20.00
Texas Rose, 1950's $10.00-15.00
Shari Lewis and Her Puppets,
  1960 . . . . *$15.00-20.00*
Carmen Miranda,1952 . $25.00-30.00

Lowe
Janie and Her Doll, 1943 $5.00-7.00.
Judy and Jack, Peg and Bill,
  1940 . . . . $25.00-30.00
Tom The Aviator, 1941 . $8.00-10.00

Giselle Mackenzie paperdolls, 1957. $15.00.

Mary Martin paperdolls, 1944. $35.00.

Uncle Sam's Little Helpers, 1943. $25.00.

Claudette Colbert paperdolls, 1943. $45.00.

A 1941 paperdoll book featuring Gloria Jean. $40.00.

Patti Page, 1957 . . . . . . $25.00-30.00
Bride and Groom, 1959 . . $5.00-7.00
Cowboys and Cowgirls,
   1950 . . . . $5.00-7.00
Let's Play House, 1940's . $4.00-6.00
Cinderella Steps Out,
   1948 . . . . $10.00-12.00
Lollypop Crowd, 1945 . $15.00-20.00
Playtime Pals, 1946 . . . . . $5.00-7.00

Merrill
Golden Girl, 1953 . . . . . $10.00-12.00
Bride and Groom, 1949 . . $5.00-7.00
Betty Grable, 1951 . . . . $35.00-40.00
Pink Prom Twins, 1956 . . $5.00-7.00
Paper Doll Family and Their Trailer,
   1938 . . . . $25.00-30.00
Big 'N' Easy, 1949 . . . . . $7.00-10.00
Baby Sisters, 1938 . . . . . $20.00-25.00
Cowboy and Cowgirl,
   1950 . . . . $5.00-7.00
Boarding School, 1942 . $15.00-20.00
Paper Doll Wedding,
   1943 . . . . $15.00-20.00

Pattern Glass
Pattern glass is clear glass with designs pressed into the glass. There are hundreds of patterns from which to choose and many pieces in each pattern. Prices vary due to scarcity and popularity of patterns as well as individual pieces.

Acanthus Leaf, goblet . $50.00-85.00
Amazon, celery $10.00-18.00
Apple Blossom,
   creamer $50.00-65.00
Banded Raindrops, sugar
   bowl $20.00-40.00

Essex and Everglades pitchers, worth $20.00-$35.00 each.

Berlin and Bevelled Diamond & Star pitchers. $30.00-$50.00 each.

Cannonball pitcher. $30.00-$50.00.

toothpick $5.00-15.00
Cabbage Rose, goblet . . $25.00-40.00
Colonial, cruet $20.00-35.00
Diamond Flute,
 compote $18.00-35.00
Eyelet, pitcher $20.00-35.00
Fan with Diamond,
 celery $10.00-18.00
Gibson Girl,
 creamer $100.00-165.00
Heavy Drape, goblet . . . $15.00-25.00
Ivy Spray, spoon
 holder $10.00-15.00
Lattice, sugar bowl $12.00-25.00
Man's Head,
 toothpick $15.00-25.00
Panelled Cane, cruet . . . $12.00-20.00
Parrot, compote $35.00-55.00
Shell & Jewel, butter
 dish $15.00-25.00
Three deer, goblet $45.00-65.00

Block Band-Squares pitcher. $20.00-$35.00.

Diamond Swag pitcher. $30.00-$50.00.

Bar & Bead, spoon
 holder $10.00-15.00
Bead & Panel,

Peanut Collectibles

Peanut machines were once as evident as the gumball machine. The old machines now bring good prices as do other collectibles related to peanuts and peanut companies. By far the most popular are Planter's items and the dapper "Mr. Peanut". Dolls, banks, salt shakers, jars, and many other items are available in this area. Some premiums are still being produced today.

This Mr. Peanut wood doll is worth about $35.00-$50.00.

Mr. Peanut plastic items. 50¢-$2.50.

Chopper, Planters,
  1930's $7.00-10.00
Jar, Planters, Peanut top
  lid $60.00-70.00
Planters, salt & pepper, "Mr.
  Peanut",
  multicolored $5.00-10.00
Planters, mechanical pencil, "Mr.
  Peanut" at end $10.00-15.00
Vending machine, Smilin' Sam,
  1930's . . . . $500.00+
Vending machine, Smilin' Sam,
  1970's . . . . $200.00+

Vending machine, Regal Hot Nut,
  glass light cover,
  1930's $50.00-75.00
Lance, large glass jar . . $25.00-35.00
Planters, ceramic
  ashtray $20.00-25.00
Planters, "Mr. Peanut" lamp,
  paper mache $150.00-175.00
Tin, Mammoth Salted
  Peanuts $50.00-55.00
Planters, "Mr. Peanut" hand puppet,
  rubber $150.00-175.00
Tin, Robison Crusoe,
  cylindrical $100.00-125.00
Planters, "Mr. Peanut" doll, wood,
  1930's $45.00-55.00
Planters, "Mr. Peanut" alarm
  clock $25.00-30.00

Philatelics

Philatelics (stamp collecting) is one of the largest collecting hobbies in existence. Postage stamps offer a colorful, historical look at the United States or the entire world. Many collectors specialize in one or more areas of this emense hobby while others collect a cross section of many types. There are some very scarce and valuable stamps but most are worth only a few cents. The material here is generally philatelic related items that have an historic or nostalgic interest as well. In spite of the many collectors, many bargains are still to be found in old papers, documents, etc.

Wells Fargo cancellation
  covers $45.00-100.00
First Flight Airmail, Oct. 28, 1928, via
  Graf Zeppelin . . . . $300.00+
Washington & Philadelphia Railroad
  cancellation, 1850's . . $50.00-60.00
Cover with R.P.O.
  postmark $3.00-10.00

An R.P.O. cachet cover from 1948 worth about $3.50.

Migratory Bird Hunting Stamps, used,
 1950's, each $3.00-5.00
Special Delivery Stamp, 10¢ blue,
 unused, 1885 .... $300.00 +
Airmail, 1918 6¢ orange,
 unused .... $150.00 +
Revenue stamp, 3¢ Telegraph,
 1860's, used $1.00-2.00
Revenue stamp, 1¢ playing cards,
 1860's, used $125.00-150.00
Stock transfer, $1 green, used,
 1920's $2.50-3.50

Phonographs and Music Boxes

The phonograph was first patented in the late 1870's and was known as the "talking machine". Cylinders, discs and records were used on the early machines and a variety of speaker devices were tried. Nearly all early types and brands of phonographs are popular today with collectors paying high prices for those in excellent condition. The prices here are for those that are in working order with no missing parts either in the working mechanism or the decorative cabinet.

The Criterion, 16", steel discs,
 oak case .... $1,000.00 +
Polyphon, 15½" discs, walnut
 cabinet .... $1,200.00 +
Regina, 8½" discs, oak
 case .... $1,000.00 +
Standard Machine Co., Model A,
 record player with
 horn .... $350.00 +
Edison Fireside Model B, brass horn,
 cylinder player $250.00-300.00
Edison Model D, oak cabinet, horn,
 cylinder player $500.00-600.00
Edison Triumph, with horn, cylinder
 player .... $1,000.00 +
Columbia, BK, horn . $300.00-350.00
Victor, table, Model E,
 horn $275.00-300.00
Adler, upright walnut case,
 21¼" discs .... $2,300.00 +
Perfection, 10½" discs,
 1890's .... $1,200.00 +
Stella console, 17½" discs, mahogany
 case .... $5,000.00 +
Victor II, horn .... $325.00 +
Komet, inlaid ivory in cabinet, 10¼"
 discs .... $800.00 +

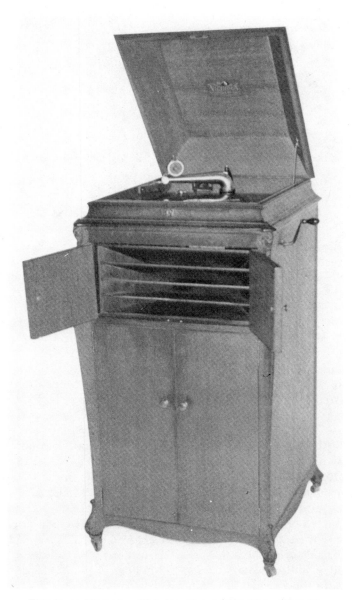

This large Victrola will bring about $225.00 to $265.00.

This Victrola is worth about $145.00-$165.00.

Victor Victrola, oak
cabinet . . . . $225.00 +

Photography
Cameras & Equipment
Cameras have become increasingly popular among collectors in recent years. There are hundreds of cameras and pieces of photographic equipment available to collectors today, due to the relative newness of the hobby. Age is not always the value-determining factor when dealing in photography equipment and prices tend to fluctuate greatly in this area. Values are for cameras in good condition.

Wetplate lens, Dallmeyer #3A,
16 " $150.00-175.00
Eastman Kodak, Graflex Series B,
1920's-1940's $70.00-80.00
Magic Lantern, 1880's . $75.00-80.00
Conley Jr., folding plate camera,
1900's $40.00-50.00
Thornton-Picard, folding plate
camera, 1890's . . . . $300.00 +
Regno cycle camera . . . $55.00-65.00
Eastman Kodak #4, black

Kodak Junior Six-20. $12.00.

This folding pocket Ansco camera from about 1915 is worth $25.00.

This Richoflex Model VII from the 1950's is valued at $25.00.

The Kodak No. 3A Autographic Model from the 1920's. $15.00.

bellows $45.00-55.00
Burke & James, No., 3, Rexo
Jr. $8.00-10.00
Rochester Optical, Long Focus Premo,
1895 ....$65.00-75.00
Kodak Century Model 47, 1907-
1926 ....$40.00-50.00

Kodak Pocket camera,
1920's $20.00-25.00
Kodak Petite $10.00-20.00
Kodak Vest Pocket,
1920's $30.00-40.00
Argus A2, 35mm, 1930's-
1950's $10.00-20.00
Mercury II CX,
1940's $20.00-25.00

Images - All prices are for photos in excellent condition. Any defects that detract from the image also reduce the price substantially. Large size photos bring more money than similar photos of smaller size. However, due to the rise in interest of antique photography as a major collecting medium and art form, values are changing every year. These rises in values are due to various factors such as personal interests of the specific collector, size of the photograph, condition, and rarity of the specific subject matter.

Daguerreotype - 1830's-1860's

The Daguerreotype, invented by Louis Daguerre in 1839, was a process in which an image was produced on a plate of copper plated with silver. It was noted for its striking clarity in detail and its mirror image. Its only difficulty was that the viewer had to turn the image at a slight angle, casting the view in a shadow, before it could be clearly seen. The Daguerreotype, being the earliest form of photography, is the rarest, and therefore, the most valuable. Basically, the values can be estimated in the following manner:

Portrait, small $7.50-50.00
Portrait, large $50.00-100.00
Portraits, famous subject . $100.00 +
Group portrait . . . . $125.00 +
Outdoor scene . . . . $150.00 +
Occupational . . . . $150.00 +
Lockets, lapel pins,
  brooches $50.00-150.00

Ambrotype - 1850's-1870's

The Ambrotype, invented circa 1850, was a form of photography produced directly on a glass plate. In actuality, it is a negative and the image is view-ed by backing the plate with black which causes the image to appear positive. Like the Daguerreotype, it was noted for its extreme clarity in detail and did, eventually, manage to replace the Daguerreotype until the invention of the tintype circa 1860. Ambrotypes compare favorably in value to Dageurreotypes but do not command quite as much money in like areas. The values can be estimated in the following manner:

Portrait, small $7.50-50.00
Portrait, large $35.00-100.00
Portrait, famous subject . . . $75.00 +
Outdoor scenes . . . . $150.00 +
Occupational . . . . $150.00 +
Jewelry $30.00-85.00

Tintype

The tintype or Ferrotype is a direct, positive image process reproduced which gave it wide popularity between 1860 and 1910. Sizes vary from 6½ "x8½ " Full Plate to the tiny 2 "x2½ " ninth plate. General value pertain to specific subject matter and can be approximated in the following manner:

Portrait, small $1.00-10.00
Portrait, large $7.50-50.00
Portrait, famous
  subject . . . . $75.00 +
Outdoor scene . . . . $100.00 +
Occupational . . . . $100.00 +

Carte-de-visite

The carte-de-visite is a positive image, reproduced by a negative, on paper. The general size of the carte-de-visite is 2½ "x3¾ " and it is mounted on a small, paper card stock measuring approximately 4 "x3 ". The name of the photographer is usually stamped on the reverse side of the card stock.

Military studio cabinet view.

Orchard

Occupational studio cabinet view.

General values basically follow those of the tintype with some slightly lower figures as paper images have not reached the popularity of the earlier, so called, "hard images" as yet. Values, as for the tintype, pertain to such standards as condition, subject matter, personal interest of the specific collector, etc. However, they can be approximated in the following manner:

Portrait $1.00-2.00
Portrait, famous
    subject $10.00-70.00
Civil War $10.00-50.00

Cabinet View
The Cabinet View is a posiitive image, reproduced by a negative, on paper similar to the carte-de-visites. However, it is a much later process, dating primarily from the 1870's to the 1920's. The general size of the Cabinet view is approximately 4″x5½″ and it is mounted on an ornate card stock of 4¼″x6½″. This ornate card stock mounting usually bears the photographer's name and address at the bottom front of the card stock, under the actual image. Values generally follow those of the carte-de-visite and can be approximated in the following manner, following the same standards as those of the cart-de-visite and the tintype:

Portrait $1.00-2.00
Portrait, famous
    subject $7.50-50.00
Outdoor scene $7.50-50.00
Western scenes (cowboys). . $50.00 +

Stereo Cards
A stereo card, when seen through the proper equipment, appears to have depth. This illusion is created by the use of side-by-side duplicate images.

Though found in metal, transparent tissue and glass, paper prints on cardboard are the most common. Lithographed cards of the late 1880's are less valuable than photo cards.

Outdoor scenes $1.00-2.00
Portrait, famous
    subject $5.00-10.00
Civil War $5.00-10.00
Lithographed cards $1.00
1850's views $12.00-17.50

Pocket Knives
Pocket knives are extremely popular trade items. Thousands of knives have been manufactured over the years, making it possible for many collectors and enthusiasts to actively participate in collecting knives. Case knives are one of the most popular brands but Remington, Winchester and others are close behind. Prices here are for used knives, sharpened, but still in excellent condition, with no blade nicks or other surface defects. Mint knives would be worth about twice as much.

A selection of pocket knives.

210

Case Hammerhead, stag
handles $25.00-35.00
Case Sharkstooth, black
handles $35.00-40.00
Case Muskrat XX, green bone
handles, 1940's . . . . $150.00+
Case Fisherman's knife, yellow
handles $10.00-15.00
Fighting Rooster,
Budding $10.00-15.00
Case Baby Scout
knife $50.00-60.00
Case Birds eye $20.00-35.00
Buck Creek, Cobra $5.00-10.00
Parker-Frost Deer-
slayer $30.00-40.00
Schrade Loveless
Hunter $65.00-75.00

Police Collectibles

Anything related to police work is collectible including badges, handcuffs, weapons, magazines, photos, paper collectibles, etc. Texas Rangers are very popular as are Chicago police items during prohibition and other eras linked to history. Many items are still reasonably priced.

Buckle, pre-1900, "POLICE" in circle of leaves $50.00-100.00
Club with cord & tassle, San Francisco, 1900's $60.00-75.00
Decal, Arizona Rangers,
small . . . . 50¢-$1.00
Handcuffs, early 1900's, with
key $60.00-75.00
Magazine, *Harpers Weekly*, March 27, 1897, traffic cop on
front . . . . $40.00+
Jail keys, old $10.00-25.00
Police Magazine, any
issue . . . . 50¢-$2.00
Police I.D. card,
1960's . . . . 50¢-$2.00
Sheet music, "Police Parade March",
1917 . . . . $20.00-25.00
Shoulder patch, Baltimore
police $1.00-3.00
Shoulder patch, Atlanta police,

A complete Gamewell police call box, used in the 1920's, is valued at $100.00.

211

Handcuffs with key, worth about $75.00.

Buckles attached to the original leather belts command a price up to $100.00.

eagle $1.00-3.00
Gamewell call box,
  1920's $75.00-100.00
Postcard, Texas Ranger,
  1940's $1.00-3.00
Book, *Twentieth Century Souvenir,*
  Boston Police,
  1901 . . . . $40.00-50.00
Buckle, "CCP", pre-1900,
  rectangle $50.00-100.00

Postcards
Postcard collecting allows the collector to view the past American life at its fullest. There are multitudes of categories available in which to specialize, or a random collection of many different types, styles, and periods, is also a valuable possession. Holiday postcards continue to be popular with collectors as do Lincoln, transportation, Indians, political, occupation, and Negro cards. Cards featuring the artist's signature have begun to gather a large following in recent years. The collector should use caution because some early cards are being reproduced. Prices here reflect cards in good condition with no tears or defacing marks. Cards showing views and street scenes of specific locations are more valuable in their respec-

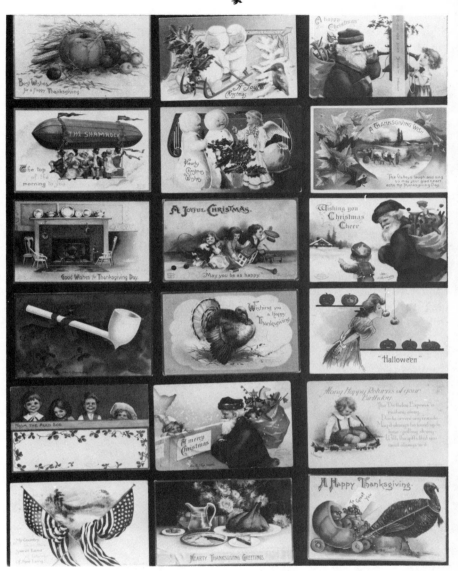

A selection of early holiday greeting postcards.

tive areas. Postcards are those with illustration on one side and space for writing on the reverse. Cards issued by the Post Office are referred to as Postal cards or postal stationery.

World War I cards $2.00-3.00

Western life $1.00-2.00
Street scenes .... 50¢-$1.00
Fire departments $3.00-7.00
Comic cards $1.00-2.00
Automobile advertising . $5.00-15.00
Ships $2.50-3.50
Lindbergh $4.00-7.00

Polictical cards $5.00-20.00
Nudes, pinups $3.00-6.50
Christmas, Santa Claus .. $1.00-3.00
Halloween $3.50-6.00
July Fourth $3.00-7.00
Easter $1.00-3.00
Birthday .... 50ᶜ-$1.50
Disaster $2.50-3.50

Primitives

Primitives are pieces, usually hand-made, that were used by pioneers 100 years ago or more. These primitives are becoming more popular as decorating accessories. Because they were generally made by hand, there is the chance that any two examples of a certain item could differ slightly. At the present time, their value is increasing but they still remain reasonably inexpensive in many cases. The collector should be very careful when buying primitives because some items are being reproduced.

Maple sugar mold, hand carved,
  1820's, hearts $125.00-150.00
Grain carrier, wood, bent handle,
  12″ deep $60.00-70.00
Trammel hooks,
  1700's $100.00-150.00
Cheese mold, wood,
  1850's $55.00-65.00
Pie peel, wrought iron,
  1800's $40.00-50.00
Cabbage cutter, wood handle, wide
  blade, 1870's $15.00-20.00
Wash tub, wood,
  1800's $70.00-80.00
Washing stick, wood,
  1890's $15.00-25.00
Lye paddle, 1800's,
  wood $40.00-50.00
Wool carder, wood with wire
  teeth $30.00-40.00
Butcher block, 20″, 3 legs,
  sycamore $200.00-250.00
Meat hooks, iron,
  1800's $15.00-25.00
Forge shovel $5.00-15.00

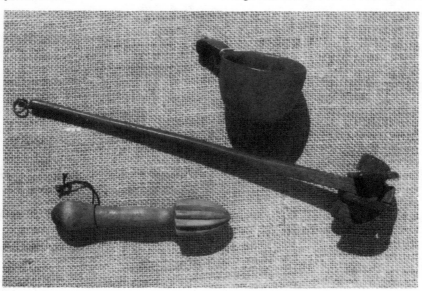

This wood porringer is worth $300.00; the swizzle stick, $45.00; the reamer, $35.00.

Primitive washboard.

Mortar & Pestle of wood. $125.00-150.00.

A large iron cauldron. $50.00.

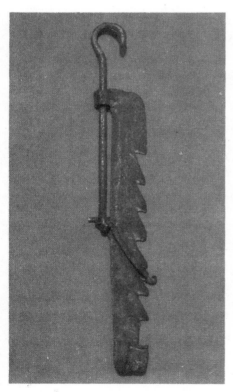
This ratchet type fireplace trammel is worth about $40.00-$60.00.

Candlestand, pine,
    1850's $150.00-200.00
Washboard, wood
    ridges $40.00-50.00
Dough raiser, cherry . . . $50.00-60.00
Candle mold, 12 stick,
    1800's $75.00-100.00
Doughboard scraper,
    iron $10.00-25.00
Child's tub, 1850's, tin . . . $200.00+
Flue rake, 1870's $3.00-5.00

Purses

Purses and handbags have only recently gained notoriety among collectors. Most types and styles back to the turn of the century and before are popular but the most sought are the metal mesh bags and beaded handbags. Many old purses used generous amounts of sterling silver, gold and stones and the prices usually reflect the material and quality of workmanship.

Victorian, black satin, glass beads,
    1890 . . . . $50.00-75.00
Coin purse, Cupid

These mesh purses, made by Mandalian and Whiting and Davis are worth $50.00-100.00 each.

Beaded handbag at left, $200.00. The others are worth about $60.00-75.00.

Beaded Handbags. Each of these is worth about $275.00-300.00.

design $40.00-50.00

Victorian, velvet, steel beads, loop
handle $50.00-75.00

Victorian, black crochet, drawstring
bag $40.00-50.00

Silver mesh, Whiting-Davis,
1910 .... $175.00-200.00

Embroidery beaded, rose design,
1910 .... $175.00-200.00

Embroidery beaded, Art Deco

clasp $75.00-100.00

Silver frame and chain, Art Nouveau,
1910 .... $75.00-100.00

Crystal beads, gilt filigree frame,
1910 .... $90.00-100.00

Victorian, gilt frame, beaded,
1900's $125.00-150.00

Quilts & Needlework

Quilts and needlework have gained

An early signature quilt. Quilts are valued according to quality, color, material and pattern.

new popularity in recent years. The presence of hand prepared work makes the quilt, sampler or rug an item that takes many hours of skilled watchful labor. The value depends on several factors. First and foremost, is the quality of work and details that have been included. Also important is the quality of material and the condition of the piece. Cross stitched coverings are generally more valuable than pieced quilts.

Broken Star, 1900's . . . . . . $200.00 +
Log Cabin, 1900's . . . . $200.00 +
Rose, cross-stitched . . . . . . $175.00 +
Tulips, 1800's . . . . $300.00 +
Star of Bethlehem . . . . $200.00 +
Sunbonnet Girls,
    applique . . . . $150.00 +
Wreath of Roses, 1800's . . $250.00 +
Feathered Star,
    recent $50.00-100.00
Wedding Ring, recent . $75.00-125.00
Honeycomb, 1800's . $125.00-150.00

Railroad Collectibles

Anything that was actually used by a railroad or anything picturing trains is considered to be a railroad collectible. Stamps, postcards, timetables, signs, lanterns, glassware, locks, water and oil cans, badges and uniforms, are all in demand from collectors of train memorabilia. Stocks, bonds, photographs and advertising material are also very popular.

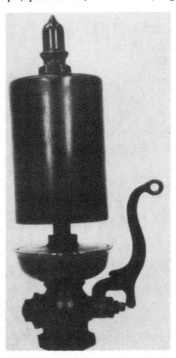

This locomotive steam whistle is worth about $125.00.

Baggage check, "B . & O. R.R."	$10.00-15.00
Badge, "Great Northern Special Police", star & shield	$90.00-100.00
Uniform button, "Missouri, Kansas & Texas"	$3.00-5.00
Calendar, Burlington Route, 1938	$25.00-30.00
Long spout oil can, "SOO R.R."	$25.00-30.00
Cap badge, "Pullman Conductor"	$20.00-25.00
Head rest, Illinois Central, 15"x15½"	$5.00-7.50
Menu, "Zephyr", luncheon, 1943	$5.00-7.50
Stir stick, "Amtrak"	$1.00-2.00
Switch key, "Adlake"	$7.00-10.00
Switch stand lamp, GNRY	$100.00-125.00
Caboose wall lamp, brass, glass chimney	$40.00-50.00

Railroad glassware. From left to right: tumbler, $6.50; cordial, $10.00; tumbler, $5.00; water glass, $8.00.

222

Ticket envelopes worth about $1.00 to $2.00 each.

This Chicago Rock Island & Pacific calendar from 1888 is worth about $100.00 unused.

Luggage sticker, "Burlington Route", Buffalo Bill $12.00-18.00

Travel folder map, "Rock Island".......$8.00-10.00

Pass, Chesapeake & Ohio RR, 1930 ....$2.00-5.00

Employee pass, Missouri Pacific, 1899 ....$8.00-10.00

Pinback button, "Amtrak" $3.00-5.00

Pinback button, Canadian Pacific, with beaver $15.00-18.00

Playing cards, C & A, cowgirl, 1900's $50.00-60.00

Bell, steam locomotive ...$600.00+

Headlight, steam locomotive, 1920's $185.00-200.00

Ashtray, G.N., china, mountain goat $60.00-70.00

Ball point pen, DM & IR $2.00-3.00

Telegraph key, brass base $35.00-40.00

Ticket punch, C.G.W., "L" mark.........$10.00-15.00

An early Bill Haley and his Comets record.

An early Eddy Arnold record.

Records

78 RPM

Louis Armstrong & His Hot Five, "Star Dust", Columbia $7.00-12.00

Cab Calloway, Brunswick label $5.00-10.00

Handy's Memphis Blues Band, "St. Louis Blues", Banner $10.00-15.00

Bing Crosby, "At Your Command", Brunswick $7.00-10.00

Carter Family, "Darling Daisies", Bluebird $5.00-8.00

Woody Herman & His Orchestra, "Double or Nothing", Decca $7.00-10.00

Harry James & His Orchestra, "Texas Chatter", Brunswick . $7.00-10.00

Memphis Jug Band, "Jazbo Stomp", Okeh $30.00-40.00

The Mills Brothers, "Diga Diga Doo", Brunswick $10.00-15.00

Tom Owens, WLS, Barn Dance Trio, "Hell on The Wabash" $5.00-8.00

Bud Richie & His Boys, "Slappin ' The Bass", Champion . . . $10.00-20.00

Jimmie Rodgers, "Prairie Lullaby", Bluebird $10.00-15.00

"Fats" Waller, "Ain't Misbehavin '", Victor $7.00-10.00

Paul Whiteman's Rhythm Boys, "Wa Da Da", Columbia . . . $8.00-12.00

Bob Wills & His Texas Playboys, "Mexicali Rose", Vocalion $8.00-12.00

45 RPM

Roy Acuff "Great Speckled Bird", Harmony $7.00-10.00

The Beach Boys, "Surfin '", Candix $40.00-60.00

Chuck Berry, "Maybelline", Chess $7.00-10.00

Fats Domino, "Ain't It A Shame", Imperial $5.00-8.00

Four Seasons, "Peanuts", Vee Jay $10.00-15.00

Lamplighters, "Yum Yum", Federal $7.00-10.00

Jerry Lee Lewis, "Crazy Arms", Sun $7.00-10.00

Carl Perkins, "Pink Pedal Pushers", Columbia $5.00-8.00

Ray Smith, "Let Yourself Go", Infinity $4.00-7.00

Spinners, "My Love and Your Love", Rhythm $30.00-40.00

Redwing two gallon crocks. $25.00.$30.00 each.

Red Wing Pottery

Red Wing Pottery from Minnesota, like other defunct potteries, is being collected across the country. Red Wing made dinnerware, crockery, cookie jars, and other practical as well as decorative pieces.

Ashtray, horse head ...$12.00-15.00
Planter, leaf shape $8.00-10.00
Planter, canoe $22.00-25.00
Cookie jar, Dutch girl .$30.00-35.00
Dinnerware, Bobwhite, salt &
    pepper $20.00-25.00
Dinnerware, Bobwhite, vinegar & oil
    in stand $35.00-40.00
Cookie jar, Friar Tuck.$35.00-40.00
Dinnerware, Tampico,
    casserole $10.00-15.00
Teapot, figural
    chicken $18.00-20.00

Redwing cookie jar. $25.00-$35.00.

Dinnerware, Magnolia,
    teapot $20.00-25.00
Sponngeware bowl,
    ovenware..........$40.00-45.00
Planter, piano shape...$12.00-18.00
2 gallon crock, leaf
    design $25.00-35.00

225

Dinnerware, Village brown, covered
baking dish $8.00-10.00
Cookie jar, chef $30.00-35.00

Rockwell Collectibles

Norman Rockwell was probably the most popular and well known American artist and illustrator of all time. His illustrations decorated the covers of *The Saturday Evening Post* for nearly half a century. Rockwell art can be seen in advertising from Coca-Cola to Ford Motor Company to Schmidts with a multitude of products in between. Rockwell art in its original use as well as figurines, plates, prints, or other reproductions are considered collectible. Keep in mind that many Rockwell products are still being manufactured.

Tray, Green Giant corn,
1940's $40.00-50.00
1927 Sears catalog

A Norman Rockwell *Saturday Evening Post* **cover, 1960.**

Postage stamps featuring Norman Rockwell designs.

cover $25.00-30.00
Cardboard sign, Arrown shirts,
  9"x12", man with hands in
  pockets $60.00-70.00
Calendar, Coca-Cola, fishing boy and
  dog, 1931 ....$125.00-150.00
Magazine ad, Quaker Puffed Wheat,
  1924, boy in tie $3.00-5.00
Puzzle, "The Treasure Chest",
  1920's $30.00-32.00
Calendar, 8"x14", Boy Scouts,
  1942 ....$10.00-15.00
Magazine ad, Post Grape Nuts,
  1919 ....$3.00-5.00
Magazine, *Saturday Evening Post*,
  May 20, 1916 .....$200.00-500.00
Magazine, *Saturday Evening Post*,
  Oct. 13, 1956,
  Eisenhower $10.00-20.00
Magazine ad, Dec. 1940, General
  Motors..............$3.00-5.00
Ad posters, early 1970's,
  McDonald's $1.00-2.00
Key chain, plastic, Ford,
  1950's $10.00-12.00

Roseville Pottery

The first Roseville pottery made was artist signed, hand painted pottery. This artist signed pottery is by far the most valuable today. Many other types of pottery were produced, both marked and unmarked, and all types are popular with collectors. The collector should be careful not to confuse the hand painted pottery with the pieces that have been decorated with transfer designs.

Rozane, ewer, 11"...$225.00-250.00
Rozane Royal, vase,
  6½" $175.00-200.00
Azurean, vase, 4½".$300.00-350.00
Egypto, oil lamp, 5".$250.00-275.00
Woodland, vase, 10".....$600.00+
Fudji, vase, 9" ....$1,000.00+
Olympic, tankard, 11"..$1,800.00+
Dogwood, wall pocket .$50.00-60.00
La Rose, bowl, 6".....$30.00-35.00
Thorn Apple, cornucopia,
  6"................$25.00-30.00
Poppy, ewer, 10" $65.00-75.00
Blackberry, candleholders, 4½",
  pair $100.00-125.00
Cherry Blossoms, jug vase,
  7"..............$100.00-125.00

Peony, 1930's ewer. $65.00-$75.00. The 8" wall pocket is worth $35.00-$40.00.

Roseville Woodland vases. $500.00-650.00 each.

Rozanne vase, $140.00-165.00; ewers, $225.00-275.00.

Roseville matte color pieces, 1916. $25.00-40.00 each.

Roseville matte green gate, 1900's. $20.00-25.00.

Wisteria, console bowl,
   12″ $75.00-85.00
Laurel, bowl, 7″ $25.00-30.00
Pinecone, triple candleholder,
   5½″ $40.00-45.00
Morning Glory, vase,
   8″ $125.00-150.00
Gardenia, basket, 8″ . . . $50.00-60.00
White Rose, flower
   frog $20.00-25.00
Water Lily, cookie jar,
   10″ $85.00-95.00
Zephyr Lily, ashtray . . . $25.00-35.00
Peony Tea set, (pot, sugar,
   creamer) $75.00-85.00
Magnolia, basket, 10″ . $75.00-85.00
Columbine, ewer, 7″ . . . $45.00-50.00
Foxglove, vase, 4″ $20.00-25.00

R.S. Prussia

Like many of the beautiful hand decorated porcelain pieces now so valuable, this was once an inexpensive import item. The high quality of the hard paste porcelain plus the beauty of

A Roseville Rozane jardiniere and pedestal. $600.00-$750.00.

Roseville Rozane pottery. The mug is worth $150.00-$175.00. The vase is valued at $150.00-$175.00 and the handled bowl is worth $225.00-$250.00.

R.S. Prussia creamer and sugar. $225.00-$300.00.

An R.S. Prussia berry set worth about $600.00-$800.00.

the hand painted decoration make pieces marked "R.S. Prussia" very popular with discriminating collectors.

Bowl, "Icicle" mold, swan design, 11"................$1,000.00+

Bowl, footed, "Icicle" mold, pheasant design, 6"........$750.00-950.00

Cake plate, "Fleur-de-lys" mold, woman, 10½"........$1,300.00+

R.S. Prussia plates. $275.00-325.00.

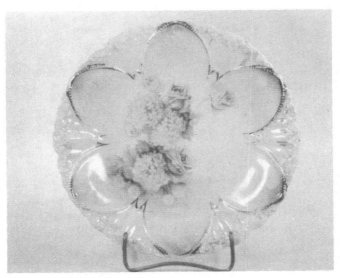

R.S. Prussia berry set. $500.00-600.00; plate, $225.00-275.00.

This R.S. Prussia toothpick holder is valued at $150.00-$200.00.

Salt Shakers

Salt shaker collecting was once considered merely a sideline to serious glassware collectors, the majority of quality salt shakers being included in collecting because of the pattern. Salt shakers have become popular in recent years in their own right. Art and pattern glass salt shakers were made in

Dice salt shaker from the 1880's. $100.00-$125.00.

Vegetable bowl, handled, "Medallion" mold, sailboat & cliffs $800.00-1,000.00

Oval bowl, "Lily" mold, portrait . . . . $1,800.00 +

Plate, 8½ ", Gibson Girl $400.00-600.00

Pitcher, 5½ ", parrots . . $1,200.00 +

Teapot, 7", Dogwood Blossoms $500.00-600.00

Sugar & creamer, castle scene & mill scene . . . . $1,000.00 +

Syrup pitcher, "Medallion" mold, Napoleon design . . $600.00-800.00

Plate, 7½ ", turkey & evergreens . . . . $1,000.00 +

Celery dish, 13½ ", melon eaters . . . . $1,200.00 +

Oval bowl, masted ship decor . . . . $1,200.00 +

Bowl, 11 ", stag scene . . . $2,200.00 +

Cake plate, 9", Victorian vignette decor $900.00-1,100.00

Pillar Ribbed salt shaker from the 1880's. $55.00-$62.00.

This Longwy salt shaker from the 1870's is valued at about $90.00.

many patterns and styles, and there are hundreds available to collectors. The collector should be cautious in buying salt shakers, because some reproductions are available.

Cotton bale, blue	$30.00-35.00
Spiderweb, pink	$35.00-40.00
Acorn, white	$50.00-55.00
Dice, white & floral	$100.00-125.00
Cornucopia, clear	$30.00-40.00
Biliken, gilt	$55.00-70.00
Corn, white	$90.00-115.00
Cut, pink translucent	$35.00-40.00
Grecian goddess, white	$35.00-40.00
Olympic games, 1932, Los Angeles	$42.00-50.00
Pig in a poke	$100.00-130.00
Refrigerator, G.E., white	$30.00-40.00
Mary Bull, rubigold	$18.00-24.00
Sphinx, clear	$65.00-75.00

Egg, flat end, white and floral $75.00-85.00

Shaker Collectibles

The Shakers, or United Society of Believers in Christ's Second Appearing, were a very simplistic religious cult that made beautiful, yet simple furnishings and tools. The furniture is without decorative accessories and is utilitarian in design. Because this furniture was of good solid construction and the group is no longer in existence, values for Shaker furniture and crafts are high. Beware of reproduction Shaker furniture and modern furniture in the Shaker style.

Berry bucket, bail handle, yellow

This Shaker canteen is valued at $175.00-$225.00.

Shaker fingered carriers from the 1800's. $450.00-$550.00.

Shaker seed boxes valued at $250.00-$550.00 each.

paint $125.00-145.00
Utility basket, wood handles,
    wrapped rim . . . . $250.00+
Seed box $250.00-500.00
Butter churn, wood, piggin
    handle $325.00-375.00
Cheese basket . . . . $350.00+
Cheese boxes, set of 3, 14″ - 18″
    eyelet hoops $800.00-900.00
Covered bucket, spout and
    handle . . . . $300.00+
Canteen, eyelet hoops, wood
    handle $175.00-225.00
Armchair, 4 slats,
    splint seat . . . . $500.00+
Pickle jar with original
    label $175.00-200.00
Footstool, splint top . $110.00-125.00
Market basket, copper
    rivets $150.00-170.00
#7 production rocking chair, slat
    back, web seat . . . . $700.00+
Apple parer, wood . . $175.00-200.00
Water bucket, banded, bail
    handle $150.00-200.00

Scoop, carved wood . $110.00-120.00
#3 production rocking chair, 3
   slats .... $300.00 +
4 drawer chest, round pulls,
   painted .... $1,000.00 +

Shawnee Pottery

Shawnee pottery was made in Ohio from 1937 until 1961. The inexpensive products of the company were sold primarily through chain and department stores. Since the closing of the pottery works in 1961, the pieces have become more popular with collectors. The most familiar pieces of Shawnee pottery are the cookie jars and the very popular "corn" pieces, made to resemble ears of corn. The salt and pepper sets of smiling pigs and sailors are also popular.

Teapot, figural Granny
   Ann $20.00-25.00
Pitcher, pig........... $20.00-25.00
Farmer pig & wife, salt
   shakers $15.00-20.00
Cookie jar, basket of
   fruit $25.00-30.00
Sugar bowl, basket of
   fruit $10.00-20.00
Mugsey dog, salt &
   pepper $15.00-20.00
Farmer pig, cookie jar . $25.00-30.00
Dutch girl, cookie jar . . $25.00-30.00
Dutch boy, cookie jar . $25.00-30.00
Planter, dog & shoe $5.00-7.00
Corn salt & pepper,
   5½ " $10.00-12.00
Corn platter $10.00-15.00
Corn butter dish,
   covered $20.00-25.00

Shawnee Pottery salt and pepper shakers.

Shawnee Pottery pig cookie jars.

Shawnee corn pieces, $10.00-20.00 each.

More Shawnee corn pieces, $10.00-20.00 each.

Teapot, figural
  elephant $10.00-12.00
Owl, salt & pepper $10.00-12.00
Owl, cookie jar $25.00-30.00
Dutch boy & girl, salt &
  pepper $5.00-10.00
Little Jack Horner, wall
  vase $5.00-10.00
Milk pail, salt & pepper . $5.00-10.00
Sprinkler can, salt &
  pepper $8.00-10.00

Sheet Music

Popularity of sheet music peaked during the "Tin Pan Alley Days," from the 1880's until the 1930's. There was fierce competition between song publishers and the graphics used to adorn the covers of the sheets are indeed works of art. Millions of pieces of sheet music were engulfed by an eager public wanting to play and sing the sad songs of the '90's, patriotic songs of the war years, and the happy, silly, or romantic songs of the times in between. Most pieces are still

"Baby Face" from 1926. This well-known song sheet is worth about $2.00-$2.50.

Music from the *Al Jolson Story*. $3.00.

priced low enough to allow many more collectors into the field.

"Anniversary Song",
  Al Jolson $5.00-7.00
"It Only Happens When I Dance
  With You", Judy Garland &
  Fred Astaire $3.00-5.00

Music from Irving Berlin's *Easter Parade*.
$2.00-$2.50.

"The Big Brown Bear", 1919. $2.00-$2.50.

Shirley Temple bath drum. $35.00.

"Baby Face", 1920's $3.00-5.00
"Careless Love",
   Lena Horne $2.00-4.00
"Cloud Kisser", 1911 .... $3.00-5.00
"Mammy Jinny's Hall of Fame",
   1917 .... $5.00-7.00
"Down on The Farm",
   1923 .... $3.00-5.00
"Happy Hooligan Dance & Two
   Step", 1907 .... $15.00-20.00
"Co-Ed", 1914 .... $2.00-3.00
"The Perfect Song", Amos &
   Andy $20.00-30.00
"By Heck" $2.00-3.00
"The Kangaroo Hop",
   1915 .... $2.00-3.00
"General Grant's March",
   1902 .... $7.00-10.00
"Don't Bring Lulu",
   1920's $2.00-3.00
"One-A-Strike", 1908 . $10.00-12.00

Shirley Temple

Shirley Temple, the dimpled little actress of the thirties, was one of the most popular performers of the day. In 1934, Ideal's first Shirley Temple doll began a flood of toys, dolls, books, cards,, pins, records and games that were immediately as popular as the cute little girl. The charm of Shirley Temple is still evident today as collectors pay premium prices for the memorabilia that is related in any way. The collector should be cautious in buying Shirley Temple items because some are being reproduced. Dolls in special clothes are worth considerably more.

Pitcher, cobalt with photo, General
   Mills premium $25.00-30.00
Mug, cobalt with photo, General Mills
   premium $25.00-30.00
Bowl, cobalt with photo, General Mills
   premium $20.00-25.00
Big Little Book, *The Little
   Colonel* $20.00-25.00
Movie Program, *Baby Take
   A Bow* $12.00-18.00
Shirley Temple on Parade soap, 5 ",
   original box $40.00-50.00
Drawing book, 1930's,
   Saalfield $25.00-30.00

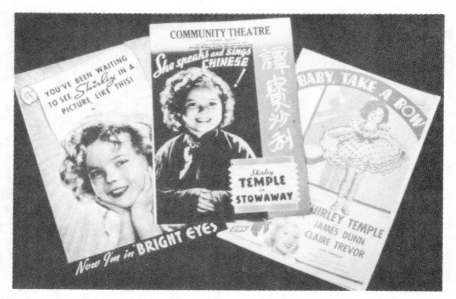

These movie programs from Shirley Temple films are worth about $15.00 each.

Shirley Temple Big Little Books by Saalfield. These books are worth about $15.00 and up, each.

Shirley Temple sheet music. $15.00-$20.00.

Photoplay, Jan. 1935, Shirley
    Temple cover $8.00-12.00
Movie display stand-up, *Little*
    Miss Marker, 6′ . .$175.00-200.00
Movie pressbook, *Our Girl*
    Shirley, 1934 . . . .$45.00-60.00
Composition dolls, mint in original

clothes with original hair set.
15″ Stand up and Cheer $425.00
27″ Baby Take A Bow $525.00
25″ Bright Eyes $500.00
16″ Heidi $475.00

13" Curly Top $475.00
16" Our Little Girl $425.00
27" Little Colonel $600.00
20" Poor Little Rich Girl . . . $450.00
22" Stowaway $450.00
20" Bluebird $650.00
Vinyl dolls, mint in original clothes with original hair set.
12" Captain January, 1958 . $125.00
15" Heidi, 1960 . . . . $150.00
15" We Willie Winkie,
    1959 . . . . $175.00
12" Rebecca of Sunnybrook
    Farm $100.00
15" Montgomery Ward,
    1972 . . . . $150.00

Silverplated Flatware

Flatware that has been silverplated is usually of good quality and very durable. The attractiveness of the design as well as scarcity and metal quality determine the value of these items. Several companies have produced silverplate from the 1800's until today.

Aurora, Empress, 1883, ice tea
    spoons $8.00-10.00
Gorham, Saxony, 1891, dinner
    fork $5.00-10.00
Gorham, Carolina, 1895, berry
    spoon $10.00-15.00
Marion Silverplate, Jewell, 1916,
    salad fork $5.00-8.00
Montgomery Ward & Co., Majestic,
    1893, tablespoon $5.00-10.00
National Silver, Florence, 1930,
    cheese knife $8.00-10.00
Oneida-Capital, Winthrop, 1929,
    teaspoon $8.00-10.00
Oneida-Community, Adam, 1917,
    dinner fork $8.00-10.00
Oneida-Community, Evenign Star,
    1950, tablespoon $10.00-12.00
Oneida-Duro Plate, Beverly, 1922,
    salad fork $5.00-8.00
Oneida-Puritan, Grape, 1913,
    luncheon fork $8.00-10.00
Reed & Barton, Sheffield, 1910,
    dinner knife $5.00-8.00
Reed & Barton, Old London,
    1936, teaspoon $7.00-10.00
W.H. Rogers, Nordica, 1890,

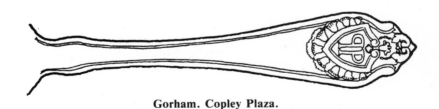

Gorham. Copley Plaza.

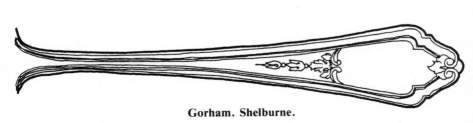

Gorham. Shelburne.

Groham. Shell. **Gorham. Blackstone.** **Gorham. Empire.**

International - Rogers & Bros. General Putman.

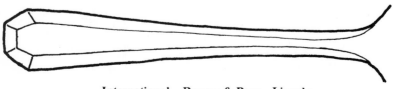

International - Rogers & Bros. Lincoln.

244

tablespoon $7.00-10.00
Tiffany, Old French, 1884,
  salad fork $6.00-8.00
Towle, Victor, 1882, dinner
  knife $5.00-8.00
Towle, Arundel, 1902, dinner
  fork $5.00-8.00

Wallace, Cardinal, 1907, ice tea
  spoon $7.00-10.00
Wallace, Alamo, 1913, sugar
  spoon $10.00-15.00
Williams Brothers, Louvre, 1907,
  dinner knife $5.00-8.00

International - Rogers & Bros. Admiral.

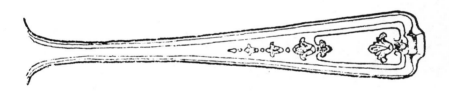

International - Rogers & Bros. Louvain.

International - Rogers & Bros. Claridge.

Sporting Collectibles

Hunting and fishing paraphernalia head the list of popular sporting collectibles but collectibles of yachting, boating, horse racing and riding, boxing, bicycling, etc., are steadily gaining ground. Just about anything remotely related to the activities are considered collectible including paintings, stamps, and figures as well as actual equipment.

Envelope, imprinted "Winchester", red & blue, New Haven postmark, 1912 . . . . $10.00-15.00

Booklet, R.C. Cola, *How To Box*, Jack Dempsey, 1930's $8.00-10.00

Reloading outfit. $75.00 and up. Winchester advertising pinback. $25.00 and up.

A carbide lantern and carbide container. $25.00-$50.00.

Program, Kentucky Derby,
1930's $10.00-15.00
Duck hunting stamp, used,
1958/59 .... $2.00-4.00
Race program, Providence, R.I.,
1902 .... $10.00-12.00
Hartland figure, plastic, Green
Bay Packer $10.00-20.00
Fishing pole, bamboo,
Payne $60.00-75.00
Miami Dolphins, 1970
guidebook $3.00-5.00
Fishing reel,
Winchester $40.00-60.00
Fishing plug, Shakespeare $2.00-5.00
Magazine, *Western Horseman*,
1890's $12.00-15.00
Trotter's Rosettes, glass,
pair $25.00-30.00
Magazine, *Sports Illustrated*,
Aug. 15, 1954 ...... $5.00-15.00
Magazine, *Boxing News*,
1935 .... $5.00-7.00
Catalog, Spalding,
1900's $5.00-10.00

Stock Certificates

Stocks and bonds collecting or "Scripophily" has only recently become popular with collectors. Most collectible stocks are no longer negotiable and factors influencing value are the type company issuing the stock, how pleasing to the eye the certificate is, signatures on the certificates, and condition. Prices here are for cancelled stocks.

Greene-Gold Silver Co.,
1908 .... $10.00-12.00
Marconi Wireless Telegraph Co.,
1912 .... $20.00-25.00
Risse Tire Corporation,
1920 .... $10.00-12.00
Franklin Fire Insurance Co.,
1930's $5.00-8.00
A.T. & T., recent $3.00-5.00
Indiana Northwest Traction Co.,
bond $20.00-25.00
Lehigh Coal and Navigation,
1913 .... $3.00-5.00

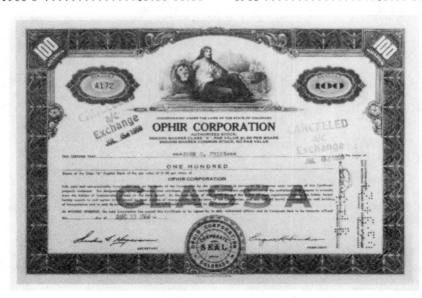

This stock certificate is valued at about $2.00.

Another stock certificate worth about $2.00.

This stock certificate is valued at about $1.00. Though some stocks are worth a lot of money, most are relatively inexpensive.

Sanitary Paper Milk Bottle Co.,
   1907 . . . . $10.00-15.00
Mission Development Co.,
   1950's $1.00-3.00
All State Credit Corporation,
   1950's $1.00-2.00

Durant Motors, Inc. . . . $15.00-25.00
Northampton Brewery Corp.,
   1930's $3.00-5.00
Beauce Gold Mining and Milling,
   1880's $8.00-10.00
Iron Clad Gold Mining . . $5.00-7.00

Telephones

Telephones have evolved over the years making the old wall and candlestick style phones very popular with collectors. There are several different makes and styles of phones on the market today but probably most popular is the oak wall phone manufactured around the turn of the century. Even cradle phones from the 1930's and 1940's are being bought by collectors, as are old switchboards and other memorabilia. Use caution when buying old telephones because reproductions are available.

Desk type, candlestick, brass, early
    1900's . . . . $125.00 +
Desk type, candlestick,
    1920's $75.00-100.00
Wall type, late 1800's, oak
    case $180.00-200.00
Wall type, early 1900's, walnut
    case $160.00-200.00
French, cradle . . . . $100.00 +
Desk type, candlestick with dial,

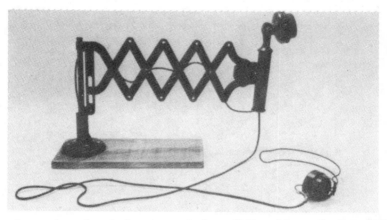

This scissors phone is a desk-mount style from 1915 and is worth about $150.00.

A Railroad dispatcher's wall phone and bell box. $225.00.

1930's $35.00-45.00
Desk type, 1930's $25.00-40.00
Bell box.............$25.00-30.00
Danish dial phone.....$30.00-40.00
Pay phone, 1920's.....$60.00-85.00
Pay phone, 1940's.....$60.00-70.00
Booth, oak, non-folding
    door ....$500.00+

Tins

Tins, or metal product containers, were used to keep contents fresh. Some have paper labels but many are lithographed onto the container. These are generally colorful, attractive containers and a wide variety is available. Be careful to avoid reissued tins and reproductions of old popular tins.

Fleischmann's Yeast,
    4"x5"x6" $20.00-25.00
Artstyle chocolate box,
    5" $8.00-10.00
Maryland Graham

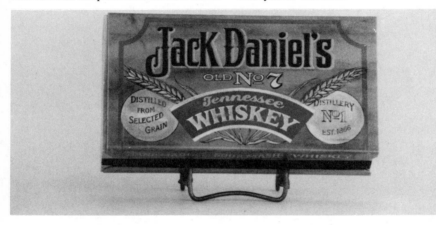

A Jack Daniels match box from the 1920's. $28.00.

Lucky Strike cigarette tin worth about $15.00-$20.00.

Sweet Cuba Tobacco tin worth about $45.00.

Wafers $15.00-20.00
Twin Oaks Tobacco . . . $20.00-25.00
Jack Sprat
   Marshmallows $20.00-25.00
Battleship Coffee $10.00-12.00
Darmody's Fine Confections,
   round $25.00-30.00
Lucky Strike Round
   100 . . . . $20.00-25.00
Lipton Orange Pekoe Tea Bags,
   1920's or 1930's $10.00-15.00
Pearson's Red Top
   Snuff $8.00-10.00
Tuxedo Tobacco, 1926 . $15.00-20.00
Stag Tobacco, pocket tin,
   stag $7.00-10.00
Blue Sultana, peanut butter
   pail $40.00-50.00
Weidman Boy Coffee, cylindrical,
   boy baker $5.00-10.00
Vermont Maple Syrup . $20.00-25.00

Tools

As mechanized labor becomes more practical in this country, the use of the hand tool sharply declined. Improvements in design and styling also contributed to the replacement of early hand tools with more modern versions. Collectors of antique tools generally use the items for decoration rather than acutal work. The prices here are for original tools with no new parts or pieces. Evidence that the tool has been used in years past adds to the over-all appeal of the piece, and a used tool is generally more in demand than a mint version.

Capenter's adze $40.00-50.00
Butteris, wood & iron . $20.00-30.00
Hoof knives $15.00-25.00
Carriage jack, oak
   and iron $60.00-70.00
Slater's pick $22.00-25.00
Buzzard's wing
   broadaxe $60.00-75.00
Barking spud, 1800's . . $40.00-55.00
Spiral auger $40.00-50.00
Trenching saw, maple,
   1840's $30.00-35.00
Cooper's pull scraper . . $22.00-25.00

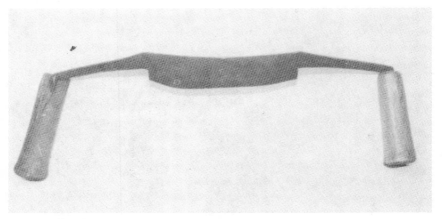

This cooper's drawknife is valued at $35.00.

Rabbet smoothing plane and rabbet plane. Each of these is worth about $18.00-$25.00.

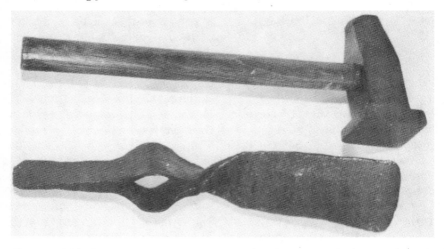

The blacksmith's flatter at top is worth about $25.00. The grubbing axe from the mid-1800's is valued at about $30.00.

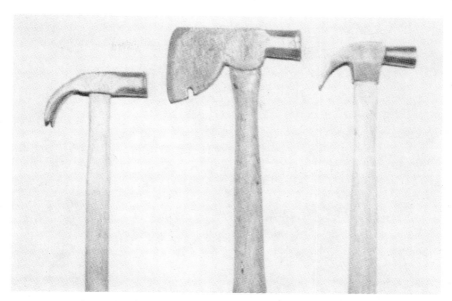

Brad, lathing hatchet, claw hammer, $8.00-15.00 each.

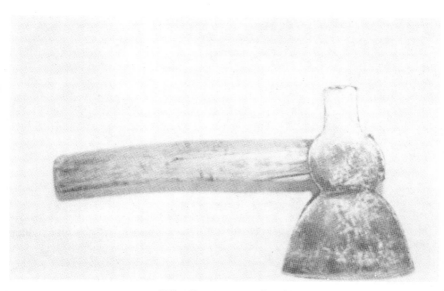

Shlingling hatchet, $15.00.

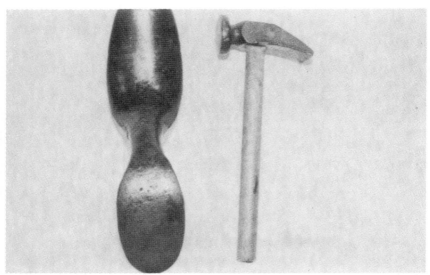

Cobbler's tools. Above: Sole cutter & mallet, $20.00-25.00 each; shoelast and hammer, $15.00-20.00.

Cooper's hand adze ...$25.00-30.00
Drawknife............$35.00-40.00
Chiming iron $40.00-50.00
Bung pick $65.00-75.00
Button tongs $12.00-15.00
Spoke rounder $15.00-20.00
Bricklayer's hammer ...$10.00-15.00
Peeling chisel, early
   1800's $50.00-60.00
Log roller, wood
   handle $10.00-15.00
Log measure.......$100.00-125.00

Toy Soldiers

Toy soldiers of lead, wood, paper, iron, tin, pewter or composition have become very popular among collec-tors. Military miniatures have always had an attraction for men and boys alike and even writer Robert Louis Stevenson was an avid wargamer.

Manoil hostess figures. In khaki the figure is rare and in other colors can bring as much as $30.00-$60.00 each.

Marx flat tin soldiers are worth about $2.00-$3.00 each.

This Britains set of Danish Army Guard Hussar Rgt. is valued at $250.00 and up.

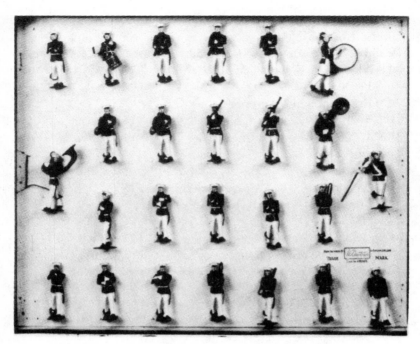

A Britain's U.S. Marine band. $1,200.00 and up.

Some of the most sought after toy soldiers are very detailed lead figures from England and those made of a wood-glue composition mixture from Germany in the 1930's. Lead casting sets for home use were sold in the 30's and 40's and they are also popular. Figures other than soldiers are collectible including bands, farm, Indians, cowboys, civilian, sports figures and others. Beware of reproduction soldiers molded in early shapes and styles. Some early plastic and rubber figures are also gaining attention.

Flag bearer on horse, Warren, lead, 1930's $40.00-50.00

Baseball player, Barclay, lead alloy................. $2.00-3.00

Marching sailor, Manoil, lead $5.00-7.00

Walking wounded soldier, Manoil, lead $5.00-7.00

Colonial Officer, Grey Iron, iron $3.00-5.00

Pirate Captain, Grey Iron, iron $7.00-10.00

Foreign Legion officer, Auburn Rubber, rubber $5.00-8.00

Football center, Auburn Rubber, rubber $3.00-5.00

Female marching saxophone player, All-Nu, lead $25.00-30.00

Grenade thrower, Jones, lead $40.00-50.00

Stretcher carrier, Playwood Plastics, composition $2.00-4.00

Machine gunner, Tootsietoy, flat metal $1.00-2.00

Trumpeter, Beton, plastic $2.00-4.00

Signal Man, Marx, lithographed tin................. $2.00-4.00

Mounted Danish army, 8 mounted figures, Britains in

box $250.00-300.00
World War I style, All-Nu,
heavy paper $2.00-3.00
Brass band, McLoughlin, paper,
1890's $1.00-1.25
Sharpshooters set, Milton Bradley,
6 paper soldiers & gun in
box $25.00-35.00
World War II front line, Built Rite,

6 paper soldiers
in box $5.00-10.00
Knight in Armor, Grey Iron,
iron $5.00-7.00

Toy Trains
Toy trains combine the lure of the
railroad with the appeal of childhood
memories for many collectors. Most

Lionel standard gauge 408E locomotive. $350.00-$800.00.

This Vulcan German live steam set from the 1890's is valued at $500.00 and up.

A Michigan Central cast iron set is worth about $250.00.

collectors are interested in the electric trains in standard gauges, but any toy train is popular. Wood and paper trains, tin, cast iron, clockwork, friction, steam or any combination is of interest to the toy train enthusiast. Though many train collectors want working examples, most are more concerned with the outward appearance of the train. Lionel trains are by far the most collected in this country, and they bring reasonably good prices.

This Tootsietoy Autogyro is valued at $30.00-$60.00.

Mechanical, Unique Art Mfg., 3-piece
    plus track $60.00-70.00
Marx double diesel, Santa Fe,
    1950's $35.00-40.00
Lionel Pullman car,
    1920's $50.00-100.00
Lionel Diesel, Flying Yankee,
    1930's $20.00-30.00
American Flyer, Silver Bullet
    train $125.00-150.00
Lionel, Hiawatha Steamer,
    1930's . . . . $250.00+
American Flyer, #21130
    locomotive $20.00-30.00
Ives, clockwork, 5 cars . . . $200.00+
American Flyer, City of Denver,
    engine, 2 cars,
    1930's $150.00-175.00
American Flyer, 0 gauge gondola
    car $10.00-12.00

Some Arcade Model T and Model A Ford cars and trucks worth from $25.00-$100.00 each.

Toys

Toys are very desirable collector's items. Most popular are the cast iron and tin toys, but those made of wood, glass, paper and celluloid are also very wise choices for the collector. To be collectible, toys must be in good condition with no missing pieces or parts and mechanical toys must be in working order. Toys fashioned after popular characters are highly prized

This Marx climbing tractor is a post-War tin wind-up toy and is worth about $25.00-$50.00.

collectibles. Military toys, animals, and vehicles make up a large portion of available toys but these are still good pieces. The collector should beware of reproduction toys.

Chein Aqua Plane,
    wind-up $50.00-60.00

Tootsietoy ships. $3.00-5.00 each.

Keystone Packard dump truck, 26″ long. $100.00-200.00.

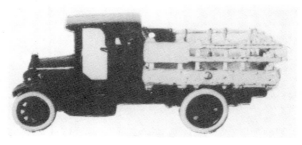

Arcade rack truck from the 1920's. This 9″ long Chevrolet truck is worth $500.00 and up.

Miniature bookcase-chest. $150.00.

An Ives U.S. Mechant Marine Boat valued at $250.00-$500.00.

Tootsietoy station wagon, rubber tires,
 1950's $10.00-15.00
Admiral Dewey's Flagship, wood
 & paper, 6″ $15.00-25.00
Pull toy, galloping horse,
 tin, 7″ $40.00-60.00
Marx Lonesome Pine Trailer & Sedan,
 19″1930's $45.00-70.00
Tonka Carnation Milk Truck, 12″,
 1950 . . . . $30.00-45.00
Kingsbury, Tin Goose Airplane,
 1930's . . . . $500.00 +
Bliss, Brooklyn Bridge, paper & wood,
 1880's . . . . $300.00 +
Carpet sweeper, Bissell . . $8.00-10.00
Pull toy, grasshopper, Hubley,
 iron . . . . $200.00 +
Kenton stove, cast
 iron $10.00-15.00
Lincoln Logs, 1920's $3.00-5.00
Marx kitchen sink,
 1950's $3.00-5.00
Marx "Pretty Maid Washing
 Machine", 1930's . . . $25.00-40.00
Monkey on a string,
 8″ $10.00-15.00
Shoenhut donkey, 10″ . $30.00-45.00
Tom Thumb cash
 register $5.00-10.00
Tool set, Greycraft, iron, steel,
 wood, 1940's $3.00-5.00
Top, wood $1.00-3.00
Battery operated Barnyard Rooster,
 1950's $40.00-60.00

Trading Cards (Non Sport)

The availability of bubble gum and tobacco cards made this collecting trend almost inevitable. There are hundreds of subjects from which to choose, the most popular being the later varities of personalities, T.V. shows, and movies. Most cards are worth only a few cents but definite increases are already apparent.

Rat Patrol, 1960's color
 photo . . . . 10¢-25¢
Monkees, 1960's color photo 25¢-50¢
Man From Uncle, 1960's, black
 and white photo . . . . 25¢-50¢
James Bond, 1965, black and
 white photo . . . . 25¢-50¢
Civil War News, 1962, color
 illustration . . . . 30¢-70¢
Batman, 1960's, color
 illustration . . . . 25¢-50¢
Three Stooges, 1950's, color
 photo . . . . 50¢-$1.00
T.V. Westerns, 1950's, color
 photo . . . . 25¢-75¢
Sea Raiders, 1930's, color
 illustrations $3.00-5.00
America At War, 1940's, color
 illustrations . . . . 50¢-$1.00
Freddie and the Dreamers, black and
 white photo, 1960's . . . . . . 10¢-25¢
Combat, 1960's, black and
 white photo . . . . 25¢-50¢

James Bond card from the movie *From Russia With Love*, 1965. 50¢-$1.00.

James Bond card from *Goldfinger*, 1965. 50¢-$1.00.

Rat Patrol **card, 1966, 50¢-$1.00.**

Planet of The Apes **card, 1967. 25¢-50¢.**

Man From Uncle Card **from 1965. 25¢-50¢.**

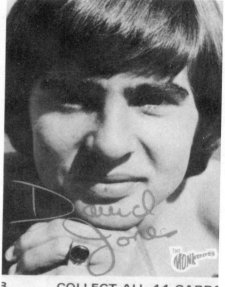

COLLECT ALL 44 CARDS

© 1966 Raybert Prod., Inc., Trademark of Screen Gems, Inc.

Monkees card from the 1960's. 25¢.

Addams Family, 1960's, black
   and white photo . . . . .25¢-50¢
Planet of the Apes, 1960's,
   color photo . . . . .25¢-50¢
McHales Navy, 1960's, black
   and white photo . . . . .10¢-25¢
Daktari, 1960's, black and white
   photo . . . . .10¢-25¢
Beverly Hillbillies, 1960's color
   photo . . . . .25¢-50¢
Good Guys & Bad Guys, 1960's color
   illustration . . . . .25¢-50¢

King Kong, 1970's color
   photo . . . . .5¢-$1.50
Hogan's Heroes, 1960, black and
   white photo . . . . .50¢-$1.50

Vernon Kilns

Vernon Kilns was a popular California pottery that is known for dinnerware as well as decorative items.
Especially popular are the theme plates
(presidents, cities, parks, etc.) and

A selection of Vernon Kilns pottery.

Walt Disney figures and items from *Dumbo* and *Fantasia*.

10½ " Kentucky plate . . $10.00-15.00
10½ " President plate . . $15.00-18.00
8½ " plates from the "Bit" series,
    each $20.00-35.00
12½ ""Remember Pearl Harbor"
    plate $20.00-25.00
10½ "Will Rogers plate . $15.00-18.00
Unicorn, Disney
    figurine $150.00-175.00
Centaurette, Disney
    figurine $175.00-200.00
Timothy Mouse, Disney

figurine $100.00-125.00
Cup & saucer set,
    Cactus $3.00-5.00
Moby Dick
    candleholders $75.00-100.00
Salt shakers, R.F.D., mail box
    shape $12.00-15.00
Sugar bowl, Brown Eyed
    Susan $6.00-12.00
Colossal cup, Tam
    O'Shanter $50.00-70.00
Platter, Pan American
    Lei $10.00-15.00
6½ " bread & butter plate,
    Chatelaine $3.00-5.00

Watches and fobs. Top row: 2 fobs; 10 jewel double case, silver, porcelain dial, $150.00; double case Swiss, 10 jewel, silver stem wind, 1890's, $125.00; English 10 jewel, 18k gold, 1870's, $350.00. **Middle row:** Elgin stem wind, 7 jewel, hunting case, 14k gold, 1870's, $350.00; hunting case, 17 jewel, 14k gold, French, $350.00; Elgin, 7 jewel, hunting case, 14k gold, 1870's, $350.00. **Bottom row:** Elgin 7 jewel, hunting case, 14k gold, $350.00; Waltham, 7 jewel, 14k gold, 1900, $350.00; Seth Thomas, 7 jewel, 14k gold, 1880's, $450.00; Waltham 15 jewel, 18k gold, $275.00; Elgin, 15 jewel, 14k gold, $350.00.

Watches

Watches hold a fascination for many American collectors. There are hundreds of old watches available but generally, the most popular are those made by Waltham, Elgin, Illinois, Dueber-Hampton, Hamilton, Howard and Seth Thomas. Values given here are for watch movements and cases in good running condition.

Watch Fobs

A watch fob is a weighted piece at the end of a watch chain or strap. They were both attractive and useful and were quite common from the late 1800's until shortly after World War I. They are usually made of brass, cast iron, bronze, copper or celluloid and are generally political, advertising or railroad in nature. Most are creative in design and because of their relatively small size can be displayed and transported easily. The collector should be cautious in purchasing watch fobs because many are being reproduced today.

Case Threading Machines, eagle
   & globe $35.00-50.00
International Harvester, hunter
   & dogs $60.00-70.00

A selection of watch fobs.

Ingersol-Rand, man &
    jackhammer $25.00-35.00
Gold Dust Twins,
    enameled $80.00-100.00
John Deere, deer jumping
    plow $35.00-40.00
Kelley-Springfield
    Rollers $30.00-35.00
P & O Plows $30.00-35.00
Mack Trucks, fire
    truck $20.00-25.00
Columbian Exposition, Keystone
    watch case $40.00-50.00
Case Tractors, early
    tractor $45.00-60.00
Caterpillar Heavy Equipment,
    Peoria, IL $15.00-20.00
Armour Packing, cow
    shape $20.00-25.00
Bell, "Ring For Ladon
    & Knox" $12.00-15.00
Spanish War Veterans, annual
    encampment $7.00-10.00

Cox & Roosevelt,
    1920 .... $135.00-150.00

Weathervanes

Weathervanes, placed on rooftops of
houses or barns were used as decoration and as indication of wind strength
and direction. Weathervanes have been
made in a variety of metals, but the
most valuable and popular seems to be
copper. Collectors should beware of
reproductions, because many early
styles are being reproduced today.

Cow, tin, small $200.00-250.00
Rooster, copper, 28" ..... $700.00+
Horse, trotting, iron . $300.00-325.00
Cow, copper .... $700.00+
Horse and rider,
    iron $250.00-300.00
Rooster, iron $150.00-175.00
Eagle on ball, copper .... $850.00+
Horse, standing, sheet

This rooster weathervane is valued at about $400.00 and up.

metal $110.00-125.00
Whale, copper .... $800.00+
Angel & trumpet,
   wood $150.00-175.00

Weller Pottery

Weller is another American pottery that made art pottery as well as inexpensive decorative pieces. Naturally the more elaborate art pieces bring the highest prices, but the less expensive pieces are being collected as well.

Cameo vase, 5″ $20.00-25.00
Patricia, bowl, 13″ duck
   heads $100.00-125.00
Drunken Ducks,
   13½″ $600.00-700.00
Louwelsa, mug, artist
   signed .... $1,000.00+
Dickensware, vase, "Chief
   Hollowhorn Bear", artist

These Weller pottery chickens are each worth about $450.00-$500.00.

The Weller Drunken Ducks are valued at $600.00-$700.00 and the Silvertone vase can be found for about $125.00-$150.00.

signed ....$1,500.00 +
Estna, vase, frog & snake,
  6½ " $165.00-195.00
Muskota, fishing boy in
  boat $100.00-125.00

Woodcraft owl vase,
  16 " $275.00-325.00
Hudson, vase, swans, artist
  signed ....$1,300.00 +
Lampbase, 14 ",

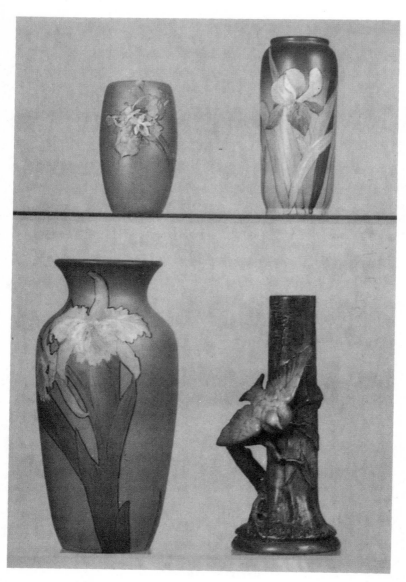

Weller Hudson pottery. Each piece is worth about $150.00-300.00.

Weller Copra vases, $100.00-150.00; Hudson vases, $125.00-150.00, $250.00-300.00.

bluebird $200.00-225.00
Coppertone, pitcher, fish
   handle $125.00-150.00
Muskota, elephant, 7½",
   tall $475.00-575.00
Garden ornament, gnome on boulder,
   18" $800.00-950.00
Sicardo, vase, 10½",
   signed $300.00-350.00
Brighton, triple wall bud vase with
   bird $225.00-250.00
Brighton, hanging parrot,
   15" $250.00-300.00
Cameo Jewell, umbrella stand,
   22" $400.00-450.00
Hudson-Perfecto, vase, 13"Arab
   on horse . . . . $2,300.00 +
Aurelian, ewer, 12"stag, artist
   signed $800.00-1,000.00
Hunter, vase, gulls, artist
   signed $450.00-550.00

Western Collectibles
The old west holds a fascination for
many collectors. Holsters, gunbelts,
cowboy equipment, guns, photography, express company collectibles
or memorabilia connected with
cowboys, outlaws, lawmen or the
western United States in the nineteenth
century is collectible. Be very careful
to avoid reproductions and fakes in
this area.

Holster, A.H. Hess & Son, Mexican
   loop $75.00-85.00
Saddle bags, "Wells Fargo & Co.",
   1880's, leather $350.00-500.00
Chaps, angora wool,
   1900's . . . . $350.00 +
Cuffs, leather,
   tooled $120.00-185.00
Coach pass, Wells Fargo & Co.,
   1900's $35.00-50.00
Wrist holster for derringer,
   leather $75.00-95.00
Cartridge belt, 55 loops,
   4¾' $50.00-85.00
Spurs, Buermann . . . . $150.00 +
Chaps, leather batwing,

This pair of early Texas spurs is valued at $275.00 and up.

272

Saloon bottles. $350.00-500.00.

Union Metallic cartridge poster. $225.00-275.00.

These angora wooly chaps from 1906 are worth $350.00 or more.

1900's $175.00-225.00
Push dagger and scabbard,
    gambler's .... $1,000.00+
Hat, Adams Express Co.,
    1900 .... $100.00-150.00
Photograph, Texas Ranger,
    1880's $350.00-400.00

Play program, "Scouts of The
    Plains", Buffalo Bill, Wild Bill
    Hickok & Texas Jack .... $250.00+
Program, "Buffalo Bill's Wild West
    Show", 1897 .... $35.00-40.00
Autobiography of William F. Cody,
    1879 .... $30.00-40.00

World's Fair & Exposition Collectibles

World's Fair and Expositions held in this country have provided collectors with many souvenirs, give-aways, and commemorative items connected with the events. These items are made of wood, glass, paper and metal, in a wide variety of categories.

Chicago, 1933, Tapestry with 3
    buildings, 20″x56″ .. $75.00-100.00
Pan American Exposition, 1901,
    souvenir booklet, 64
    pages $10.00-12.00
Pan American Exposition, 1901,
    sketch book, 24 pages . $5.00-7.50
Pan American Exposition, 1901, book
    by Buffalo Evening News, 80

A tooled leather holster worth about $45.00-$55.00.

World's Fair pinback buttons. $3.00-$5.00 each.

THE FERRIS WHEEL,
MIDWAY PLAISANCE,
WORLD'S COLUMBIAN EXPOSITION,
CHICAGO, 1893.

A photo of the Ferris Wheel at the World's Columbian Exposition, 1893.

pages $8.00-12.00
Chicago, 1933, *Official Guide Book to the Fair* $3.00-5.00
World's Exposition, Paris, 1900, *The Parisian Dream City* . $10.00-15.00
Columbian Exposition, 1893, Japanese Tea Home broadside $10.00-12.00
Pan American Exposition, 1901, paper & wood fan $12.00-15.00
Centennial Exposition, 1876, guide book with map $10.00-15.00
Centennial Exposition, 1876, 4 page newspaper supplement $25.00-30.00
Centennial Exposition, 1876, admission ticket $10.00-15.00
Chicago, 1933, playing cards with view of fair $10.00-12.00
Columbian Exposition, 1893, Clark's Thread cards, views of fair $8.00-10.00
Golden Gate, 1939, decal for car windshield $5.00-10.00
Jamestown Exposition, 1907, souvenir booklet $10.00-12.00
Louisiana Purchase, 1904, blotter, Easterbrook pens $5.00-7.00
Louisiana Purchase, 1904, guide book $4.00-5.00

New York World's Fair, 1939, official guide book, 256 pages $10.00-15.00
New York World's Fair, 1939, City of Light album, 24 pages $7.00-10.00
Panama-Pacific, 1915, Remington Typewriter souvenir booklet $15.00-20.00
Panama-Pacific, 1915, folding map $10.00-12.00
Seattle, 1962, official guide book $3.00-5.00
Pan American, 1901, official miniature view booklet $8.00-10.00
New York World's Fair, 1939, auto map in envelope $2.00-3.00
Centennial Exposition, 1876, view booklet $5.00-7.00

For more extensive information on the subjects included in the *Flea Market Trader* the following books offer illustrations and current values. The books below are currently in print and may be purchased at leading bookstores or ordered direct from Collector Books, P.O. Box 3009, Paducah, Kentucky 42001. Please ad $1.00 for postage and handling.

Advertising Collectibles
Old Advertising Jim Cope .. $9.95

Akro Agate
The Collector's Encyclopedia of Akro Agate Gene Florence $9.95

Autographs
Paper Collectibles Robert Connolly $9.95

Avon
Avon Bottle Collectors Encyclopedia Bud Hastin $19.95

Badges
Police Relics George Virgines $5.95

Banks, Mechanical
Collecting Toys Richard O'Brien $9.95

Baseball Cards
American Premium Guide To Baseball Cards Ron Erbe $14.95

Baskets
The Basket Book Don & Carol Raycraft $5.95
Collectors Guide To Kitchen Antiques.............. $17.95

Beer Cans
The American Beer Can Encyclopedia Thomas Toepfer ... $7.95

Beer Collectibles
Old Advertising Jim Cope .. $9.95

Black Glass
Black Glass Margaret James $5.95

Blue & White Stoneware
Blue & White Stoneware Kathryn McNerney $9.95

Blue Ridge Dinnerware
Blue Ridge Dinnerware Bill & Betty Newbound $8.95

Bottles
Bottle Pricing Guide Hugh Cleveland $7.95

Carnival Glass
The Standard Encyclopedia of Carnival Glass Bill Edwards . $24.95
The Standard Carnival Glass Price Guide Bill Edwards $3.95
Imperial Carnival Glass Bill Edwards $9.95
Fenton Carnival Glass Bill Edwards $9.95
Millersburg, Queen of Carnival Glass Bill Edwards $9.95
Northwood, King of Carnival Glass Bill Edwards $9.95

Character Collectibles
Collecting Toys Richard O'Brien $9.95

Clocks
The Standard Antique Clock Value Guide Alex Wescot $11.95

Coca-Cola Trays
Old Advertising Jim Cope .. $9.95

Coffee Mills
Coffee Mills Terry Friend .. $5.95

Coin Operated Machines
American Premium Guide To Coin Operated Machines Jerry Ayliffe $9.95

Collector Prints
Collector Prints, Old & New Carl Luckey $14.95

Crockery
Decorated Country Stoneware Don & Carol Raycraft $5.95
The Collectors Guide To Kitchen Antiques Don & Carol Raycraft $17.95

Cut Glass
The Standard Cut Glass Value Guide Jo Evers $8.95

Depression Glass
The Collectors Encyclopedia of Depression Glass Gene Florence $17.95
Elegant Glassware of the Depression Era Gene Florence $17.95
Pocket Guide To Depression Glass Gene Florence $9.95
Kitchen Glassware of the Depression Years Gene Florence $17.95

Disney
Collecting Toys Richard O'Brien $9.95

Dolls
Advertising Dolls Joleen Robison & Kay Sellers............. $9.95
Antique Collectors Dolls Vol. I & II
Patricia Smith ..... $17.95 each
Armand Marseille Dolls Patricia Smith $9.95
Barbie Dolls Paris, Susan, Carol Manos $5.95
Effanbee, Dolls That Touch The Heart Patricia Smith $19.95
French Dolls, Second Series Patricia Smith $9.95
German Dolls, Second Series Patricia Smith $9.95
Kestner and Simon & Halbig Dolls Patricia Smith $7.95
Madame Alexander Collector Dolls Vol. I & II Patricia Smith $19.95 Each
Madame Alexander Ladies of Fashion Marjorie Uhl ... $19.95
Madame Alexander Price Guide Patricia Smith $3.95
Modern Collector Dolls Vol. I-IV Patricia Smith..... $17.95 Each
Oriental Dolls Patricia Smith $8.95
Patricia Smiths Doll Values, Antique to Modern I & II ... $8.95 Each
Standard Antique Doll Value Guide $7.95
Standard Modern Doll Value Guide $7.95
Trolls Susan Miller $5.95

Elvis Collectibles
Elvis Collectibles Rosalind Cranor $12.95

Farm Collectibles
Collecting Farm Antiques Lar Hothem $10.95

Fiesta
The Collectors Encyclopedia of Fiesta Sharon & Bob Huxford $9.95

Franciscan Ware
Franciscan Ware Deleen Enge $9.95

Fruit Jars
1000 Fruit Jars Bill Schroeder $4.95

Furniture
The Collectors Guide To Kitchen Antiques Don & Carol Raycraft $17.95
The Oak Book Jane Fryberger $5.95
The Wicker Book Jane Fryberger $5.95
Marketplace Guide to Oak Furniture Peter Blundell $17.95
Marketplace Guide to Victorian Furniture Peter Blundell & Phil Dunning $17.95
Antique Oak Value Guide Conover Hill $7.95
Victorian Furniture, Our American Heritage Kathryn McNerney $9.95

Glass Candlesticks
The Collectors Encyclopedia of Glass Candlesticks Margaret & Douglas Archer $19.95

Guns
Modern Guns Russell & Steven Quertermous $11.95

Hummel Figurines
Hummel Figurines Carl Luckey $9.95

Indian Artifacts
North American Indian Artifacts Lar Hothem $9.95

Jewelry
100 Years of Collectible Jewelry Lillian Baker $9.95
Art Nouveau, Art Deco Jewelry Lillian Baker $9.95

Kitchen Collectibles
The Collectors Guide to Kitchen Antiques Don & Carol Raycraft $17.95

Limoges
The Collectors Encyclopedia of Limoges Porcelain Mary F. Gaston $19.95

Magazines
Paper Collectibles Robert Connolly $9.95

Majolica
Majolica Pottery Mariann Marks $9.95

McCoy Pottery
The Collectors Encyclopedia of McCoy Pottery Sharon & Bob Huxford $19.95

Medical Collectibles
Medical, Dental, Pharmaceutical Collectibles Don Fredgant $9.95

Military Collectibles
World War II German Military Collectibles Robert McCarthy $6.95

Metal Molds
Metal Molds Eleanor Bunn . $5.95

Nippon
The Collectors Encyclopedia of Nippon Porcelain I & II Joan Van Patten . . . . $19.95 Each

Occupied Japan
The Collectors Encyclopedia of Occupied Japan I & II Gene Florence $12.95 Each

Paper Dolls
Collectors Guide to Paper Dolls Mary Young.................. $9.95

Pattern Glass
The Collectors Encyclopedia of Pattern Glass Mollie H. McCain $12.95
The Standard Pattern Glass Price Guide Mollie H. McCain . $5.95

Police Collectibles
Police Relics George Virgines $5.95

Primitives
Primitives & Folk Art, Our Handmade Heritage Catherine Thuro $17.95
Primitives, Our American Heritage Kathryn McNerney....... $8.95

Purses
Antique Purses Richard Holiner $9.95

Railroad Collectibles
Railroad Collectibles Stanley Baker $8.95

Rockwell Collectibles
Norman Rockwell Collectibles Carl Luckey $9.95

Records
American Premium Record Guide Les Docks $14.95

Red Wing
Red Wing Pottery Dolores Simon $8.95

Roseville Pottery
The Collectors Encyclopedia of Roseville I & II Sharon & Bob Huxford .... $19.95 Each

R.S. Prussia
The Collectors Encyclopedia of R.S. Prussia Mary F. Gaston . $24.95

Salt Shakers
The World of Salt Shakers Mildred & Ralph Lechner $9.95

Shaker Collectibles
Collectors Guide to Kitchen Antiques Don & Carol Raycraft .. $17.95

Shirley Temple
Shirley Temple Dolls & Collectibles I & II Patricia Smith $17.95 Each

Silverplated Flatware
Silverplated Flatware Tere Hagen $14.95

Tools
Antique Tools, Our American Heritage Kathryn McNerney $8.95

Toy Soldiers
Collecting Toys Richard O'Brien $9.95

Toy Trains
Collecting Toys Richard O'Brien $9.95

Toys
Collecting Toys Richard O'Brien $9.95

Vernon Kilns
Versatile Vernon Kilns Maxine Nelson $9.95

Weller Pottery
The Collectors Encyclopedia of Weller Pottery Sharon & Bob Huxford $24.95

ILLUSTRATION ACKNOWLEDGEMENTS

Page No.

7   *Old Advertising*, Jim Cope, courtesy Great American Publishing Co.

10   *The Collector's Encyclopedia of Akro Agate*, Gene Florence

11-12   *Paper Collectibles*, Robert Connolly, courtesy Books Americana

13   *Collectors Identification & Value Guide to Antiques*, Lar Hothem, courtesy Books Americana

14   *World War II German Military Collectibles*, Robert McCarthy

15   *Bottle Pricing Guide*, Hugh Cleveland

16-17   *Police Relics*, George Virgines

18-19   *Collecting Toys*, Richard O'Brien, courtesy Books Americana

19   *Collectors Identification & Value Guide to Antiques*, Lar Hothem, courtesy Books Americana

21-23   *American Premium Guide to Baseball Cards*, Ron Erbe, courtesy Books Americana

25-28   *The Basket Book*, Don & Carol Raycraft

30-32   *American Beer Can Encyclopedia*, Thomas Toepfer

35   *Primitives, Our American Heritage*, Kathryn McNerney

37-38   *Black Glass*, Margaret James

39-43   *Blue & White Stoneware*, Kathryn McNerney

44-45   *Blue Ridge Dinnerware*, Bill & Betty Newbound

45-46   *Bottle Pricing Guide*, Hugh Cleveland

47   *Primitives, Our American Heritage*, Kathryn McNerney

48   *Paper Collectibles*, Robert Connolly, courtesy Books Americana

49-50   *Buttermolds*, James E. Trice

51-52   Hakes Americana & Collectibles, P.O. Box 1444 York, PA 17405. Mr. Hake has authored two standard references on pinback buttons. Each book pictures and prices over 4,000 buttons. *The Encyclopedia of Political Buttons* is in full color and available for $10.50 postpaid. *The Button Book* is on all types of pinbacks and is available for $6.50 postpaid. A sample copy of Hake's Sale and Mail Auction catalog is available for $1.00.

55-56   *The Standard Carnival Glass Encyclopedia*, Bill Edwards

61   *Collecting Toys*, Richard O'Brien, courtesy Books Americana

64-66   *Old Advertising*, Jim Cope, courtesy Great American Publishing Company

68-69   *Coffee Mills*, Terry Friend

70   *American Premium Guide to Coin Operated Machines*, Jerry Ayliffe, courtesy Books Americana

71-74   *Collector Prints Old & New*, Carl Luckey, Books Americana

78   Hakes Americana & Collectibles. (See acknowledgements for page 51-52)

80-81   *The Standard Cut Glass Value Guide*, Jo Evers

82   *Primitives & Folk Art, Our Handmade Heritage*, Catherine Thuro

83-98   *Pocket Guide to Depression Glass*, Gene Florence

100   *Collecting Toys*, Richard O'Brien, courtesy Books Americana

101   *Advertising Dolls*, Joleen Robison & Kay Sellers

102-103 *Patricia Smiths Doll Values, Antique to Modern*, Patricia Smith

104-105 *Armand Marseille Dolls*, Patricia Smith

106-108 *Barbie Dolls*, Paris, Susan, & Carol Manos

109-110 *Patricia Smith Doll Values, Antique to Modern*, Patricia Smith

111   *French Dolls, Second Series*, Patricia Smith

112-113 *German Dolls, Second Series*, Patricia Smith

114   *Kestner and Simon & Halbig Dolls*, Patricia Smith

115   *Madame Alexander Collector's Dolls*, Patricia Smith

116   *Patricia Smith Doll Values, Antique to Modern*, Patricia Smith

117-118 *Oriental Dolls*, Patricia Smith

119-120 *Kestner and Simon & Halbig Dolls*, Patricia Smith

121   *Trolls*, Susan Miller

121-124 *Elvis Collectibles*, Rosalind Cranor

125-126 *Antique Tools, Our American Heritage*, Kathryn McNerney

127-128 *The Collectors Encyclopedia of Fiesta*, Sharon & Bob Huxford

129   *The Collectors Guide to Kitchen Antiques*, Don & Carol Raycraft

131-132 *Fountain Pens*, Cliff Lawrence

133   *Franciscan Ware*, Deleen Enge

135-136 *The Collectors Guide to Kitchen Antiques*, Don & Carol Raycraft

137-140 *Marketplace Guide to Oak Furniture*, Peter Blundell

140   *Marketplace Guide to Victorian Furniture*, Peter Blundell & Phil Dunning

141   *Victorian Furniture, Our American Heritage*, Kathryn McNerney

142-143 *The Wicker Book*, Jane Fryberger

144   *Old West Antiques and Collectibles*, courtesy Great American Publishing Co.

145   *Primitives & Folk Art, Our Handmade Heritage*, Catherine Thuro

146   *The Collectors Encyclopedia of Glass Candlesticks*, Margaret & Douglas Archer

149-152 *Modern Guns*, Russell & Steven Quertermous

153   *100 Years of Collectible Jewelry*, Lillian Baker

154-155 *Collectors Encyclopedia of Hull Pottery*, Brenda Roberts

156-157 *Hummel Figurines*, Carl Luckey, courtesy Books Americana

160-161 *North American Indian Artifacts*, Lar Hothem, courtesy Books Americana

168-169 *Early Twentieth Century Lighting Fixtures*

172-174 *Collectors Encyclopedia of Limoges Porcelain*, Mary F. Gaston

175-176 *Collectible Locks*, Richard Holiner

177 *Paper Collectibles*, Robert Connolly, courtesy Books Americana

180 *Collectors Encyclopedia of Akro Agate*, Gene Florence

181-184 *Collectors Encyclopedia of McCoy Pottery*, Sharon & Bob Huxford

187 *Metal Molds*, Eleanor Bunn

188-189 *World War II German Military Collectibles*, Robert McCarthy

190-191 *Antique Tools, Our American Heritage*, Kathryn McNerney

192-195 *Collectors Encylopedia of Nippon*, Second Series, Joan Van Patten

195-196 *Collectors Encyclopedia of Occupied Japan*, Gene Florence

196-199 *Collectors Guide to Paper Dolls*, Mary Young

200-201 *Standard Pattern Glass Price Guide*, Mollie McCain

202 *Advertising Dolls*, Joleen Robison & Kay Sellers

203 *Railroad Collectibles*, Stanley Baker

204-205 *Marketplace Guide to Victorian Furniture*, Peter Blundell & Phil Dunning

206 *Vintage Cameras & Images*, John Maloney, courtesy Books Americana

211-212 *Police Relics*, George Virgines

214-217 *Primitives & Folk Art, Our Handmade Heritage*, Catherine Thuro

218-220 *Antique Purses*, Richard Holiner

221 *Primitives & Folk Art, Our Handmade Heritage*, Catherine Thuro

222-223 *Railroad Collectibles*, Stanley Baker

224 *American Premium Record Guide*, Les Docks, courtesy Books Americana

225 *Red Wing Pottery*, Dolores Simon

226 *Norman Rockwell Collectibles*, Carl Luckey, courtesy Books Americana

227-230 *Collectors Encyclopedia of Roseville Pottery*, Sharon & Bob Huxford

231-234 *Collectors Encyclopedia of R.S. Prussia*, Mary Gaston

234-235 *World of Salt Shakers*, Mildred & Ralph Lechner

235-236 *Collectors Guide to Kitchen Antiques*, Don & Carol Raycraft

237-239 *Shawnee Pottery*, Dolores Simon

240-241 *Collectors Identification & Value Guide to Antiques*, Lar Hothem, Books Americana

242 *Shirley Temple Dolls & Collectibles*, Patricia Smith

243-245 *Silverplated Flatware*, Tere Hagen

247-248 *Paper Collectibles*, Robert Connolly, courtesy Books Americana

249 *Railroad Collectibles*, Stanley Baker

252-254 *Antique Tools, Our American Heritage*, Kathryn McNerney
255-256 *Collecting Toys*, Richard O'Brien, courtesy Books Americana
257   *Railroad Collectibles*, Stanley Baker
258-261 *Collecting Toys*, Richard O'Brien, courtesy Books Americana
265   *Versatile Vernon Kilns*, Maxine Nelson
266   *One Hundred Years of Collectible Jewelry*, Lillian Baker
268   *Primitives & Folk Art, Our Handmade Heritage*, Catherine Thuro
269-271 *Collectors Encyclopedia of Weller Pottery*, Sharon & Bob Huxford
272-275 *Old West Antiques & Collectibles*, courtesy Great American Publishing Co.
276   Hakes Americana & Collectibles. (See acknowledgements for page 51-52)

INDEX

Advertising Collectibles 7-9
Akro Agate.. 10-11
Autographs... 11-12
Automobile Collectibles 12-13
Aviation 13-14
Avon 14-15

Badges 15-17
Banks, Mechanical 18-19
Banks, Still.. 19-20
Barber Collectibles 20-21
Baseball Cards 21-23
Baseball Collectibles 23-25
Baskets 25-28
Beatles.. 29
Beer Cans 30-33
Beer Collectibles 33-35
Bells 35-36
Big Little Books 36-37
Black Glass.. 37-39
Blue & White Stoneware 39-44
Blue Ridge Dinnerware 44-45
Bottles 45-47
Boxes 47-48
Boy Scouts 48-49
Butter Molds 49-51

Campaign Buttons.. 51-53
Campaign Collectibles 53-54
Candy Containers 54-55
Carnival Glass 55-57
Catalogs 57-60
Character Collectibles.. 60-61
Clocks 61-62
Coca-Cola Collectibles 63-64
Coca-Cola Trays 64-67
Coffee Mills 67-69
Coin-Operated Machines 69-70
Collector Prints 71-74
Comic Books 74-77
Cowboy Collectibles 77-78
Crockery 78-80
Cut Glass 80-82

Decoys 82-83
Depression Glass 83-99
Disney 99-100
Dolls, Advertising 100-102
Dolls, Antique 102-103
Dolls, Armand Marseille 103-105
Dolls, Barbie 105-109
Dolls, Effanbee 109-110
Dolls, French 110-112
Dolls, German 112-113
Dolls, Kestner 113-114
Dolls, Madame Alexander 114-116
Dolls, Modern 116-117
Dolls, Oriental 117-118
Dolls, Simon & Halbig 118-120
Dolls, Trolls 120-121

Elvis Collectibles 121-125

Farm Antiques 125-126
Fiesta 126-128
Fire Fighting 128-129
Flow Blue 129-130
Fountain Pens 130-132
Franciscan Ware 132-134
Fruit Jars 134-135
Furniture, Country 135-136
Furniture, Oak 136-140
Furniture, Victorian 140-142
Furniture, Wicker 142-143

Gambling Devises 143-145
Games 145-146
Glass Candlesticks 146-147
Graniteware 147-149
Guns 149-152
Hatpin Holders 152
Hatpins 152-154
Hull Pottery 154-156
Hummel Figurines 156-160

Indian Artifacts 160-161

Jewelry 161-165

Kitchen Collectibles 165-167